January River

BERNARD JAN

January River
by
Bernard Jan

Published by Bernard Jan, Zagreb, 2020
Originally and first published in Croatian as *January River* by
Epifanija, Zagreb, 2007, ISBN 978-953-7077-07-5

www.bernardjan.com

This is not a true story.
All characters in this work are fictitious. Any resemblance to
actual persons, living or dead, is purely coincidental.

Translated into English by Dragan Tomaševski and Bernard Jan
Editing by Trish Reeb
Proofreading by the Hyper-Speller at wordrefiner.com
Cover design by Domi at Inspired Cover Designs

ISBN (Print On-Demand) 978-953-59581-5-4

Cataloguing-in-Publication data available in the Online Catalogue of
the National and University Library in Zagreb under CIP record
001059012.

Table of Contents

To the silent nightingales
of my childhood

1

Ethan McCoy lay in the grass, stretched out to his full length. He flung his head back and unbuttoned his shirt, exposing his neck and the pale skin of his chest to the sun. His rolled-up sleeves were already drenched in sweat. Perspiration ran off his forehead, dripping onto the jacket folded under his head in a faux pillow.

Ethan removed the light-sensitive glasses from his nose and wiped the sweat off with a handkerchief. Inhaling deeply, he stared at the sun through unprotected eyes. The scent of Greenfield invaded his nostrils, conquering his throat, lungs, and heart. Inside him the memories were waking up, ignited by familiar feelings from the past.

In the strong light he felt a pain in his eyes, forcing him to close them. So that he might suffer too, he didn't move to escape into the protective shadows. Determined to stay exposed to heat that reached him from the vast distance with such strength, he willed the sun to cause him pain. Wanted it to numb his senses and make him oblivious to any and all experiences—both pleasant and unpleasant. Most of all, he wanted to let go of the internal pain that refused to leave him alone after all these years.

He wished one pain could soothe another. The physical

could annul the emotional. Even as he thought it, he knew it was in vain. He also accepted there was no cure for that pain. At best, it might be blunted some day and become just a painful reminder of his past.

But it would never disappear.

Because if it did, Greenfield would no longer exist. The artificially created grove beside the river in which he now rested, would vanish too. The same for Willy, then Jason, Derrick, and Sarah. Riv and . . . Susan. Could they evaporate, all of them? Did he have the right to ask that?

Or, what if it were possible for *all of them* to remain in their reality where they belonged? While *he*—Ethan—disappeared? Both could be possible only by some supernatural phenomenon. Something that could never happen.

Eventually moving into the shadows, he took off his shirt, shoes and socks and continued with his fantasy. Recalling. Or gathering up the strength and determination to do what he intended. Well, that's what he planned on saying if someone asked him why he was there. So far, nobody had. Nobody knew. He arrived less than an hour ago. He hadn't gone to the town, but had come straight to the river. To the place where everything had begun. Therefore, it only seemed fitting that it be where the beginning of the end transpired. The place where he would insert a period at the end of a life story. If he got lucky, he'd tear out a blank page and start anew. No memories. No past.

Without the bad memories, he could live in peace.

However, if he were honest with himself, that would be equally impossible to achieve.

In the still air, the river flowed quietly. Steadily. Innocently. Nothing about it had changed as if nothing happened. Effortlessly and seemingly without concern, the river continued to give life to all around it. But also taking it. . . .

Ethan watched the river and felt as though the river also

observed him. Two silent witnesses, side by side again after so much time. Ethan had often wondered what this moment would be like. Would he find the river repelling, disgusting even, carried by the ravages of time and pressured by anxiety heavy as storm clouds? Or would it be seductive like it had been long ago when he was still a child?

Removing the rest of his clothes, he stood on the sand along the riverbank. The sunbeams warmed his naked body—a body weakened and slimmed by an avalanche of past events. He walked into the cold water up to his knees and shuddered. Almost icy. Or was he too hot after basking in the sun?

He barely hesitated before plunging in. He knew he wouldn't be able to resist the temptation. Love between the river and him could not dissipate that easily. As he swam, he wondered if this love would ever dissolve. Would another separation be even harder than the last?

Not far away, a dog gave up chasing a butterfly. Pricking up his ears and staring toward the woods, he searched the spot where his guardian had lain only a moment ago. Except for a heap of clothes tossed on the grass, the spot was empty. Sniffing the air, the dog moved toward the river—slowly at first and then breaking into a run.

Reaching the riverbank, he looked at the water. He gazed at the other bank. No sign of life on the river. Only the nature, butterflies, and the twittering of the birds. He wagged his tail and whined. Then he barked. Soon, he ran up and down the riverbank not knowing what to do. His barking became louder and uneasy. He decided to jump and was already in the air when Ethan surfaced, with no way to avoid the collision.

The sound of the dog's whine mingled with a yell of surprise filled the air before it was swallowed and disappeared in the splash of water. The waves rippled its calm surface.

~

A bit later, the sun warmed their bodies, drying them. Unlike the golden retriever's thick hair, Ethan was already dry as dust. Holding the dog's head in his lap, he babbled to him, "Riv, you big, mischievous, hairy maniac. We could both have been killed. What came over you? Why did you do that?"

The dog murmured away contentedly, positioning his head for Ethan so he could scratch the itching spots. Gone were the uneasiness and worries that made him jump. He enjoyed every one of Ethan's strokes feeling both safe and beloved, and returning those feelings of love and safety in the same measure.

Ethan leaned in and kissed his forehead. "I love you, buddy. What would I do without you?" You are the only one who didn't desert me, he said to himself with sadness.

He closed his eyes. The breeze tousled his brown, but graying hair. For a moment, the welcome freshness of the air invigorated his soul full of melancholy and sorrow.

2

He saw his brother's face in a haze. He was smiling. The well-known eyes were blue. Blue and deep. How much uneasiness, how many sleepless nights and what amount of the guilty feeling hid behind them? The same as in Ethan? Less? More? God himself knew. They were beautiful, despite all that. They were like Ethan's, except darker. More serious. Ethan liked them.

Ethan loved his brother as much as anyone could love a brother. A corny thing to say, but true. Too many years had passed since the last time they were together. Where was Willy now? When he heard from him last, he was in Acapulco, according to the postcard he sent from there. With a few words and the inevitable, *I love you, bro*. All his postcards ended with *I love you, bro*. Hamburg. Oslo, London, Montevideo, Santos, Rio de Janeiro. *I love you, bro*. Bangkok, Hong Kong, Brisbane, Melbourne, Dakar. *I love you, bro*. Durban, New Orleans, Baltimore. . . . As if Ethan didn't know his brother loved him. That was nice to hear, anyway. Ever again. Whenever Will wrote those words at the bottom of the postcard, Ethan knew he was not just writing it, but his brother indeed felt that way. Ethan could hear the love in his voice when they talked over the phone. God, how he missed him.

He would much prefer being together than separated by many miles. Ethan needed him. Who could tell which harbor would be the next one from which the postcard would come? Their past bound them together at this precise moment in time and the memory of a rafting adventure which took place too many years ago.

Ethan was twelve back then and Will fourteen. They'd set off from the same sandbank Ethan and Riv left moments ago. It was their first ride on the raft they still tested. And they were alone. If the raft passed the test, if it wouldn't capsize or run aground and break apart, they would take the rest of the party for a ride too.

They progressed with no difficulties. Actually, Ethan thought they sailed rather smoothly. Like real rafters, or true sailors. His captain Willy and himself. Just like Tom Sawyer and Huckleberry Finn. Ethan's gaze sailed over the landscape they passed, holding steady on his brother's neck. Heavy wet curls, black coal in color, glittered in the morning sun and curled down Will's neck like baby snakes. Ethan noticed his brother's neck getting fuller and stronger with each day. The same with his well-built shoulders and the chest, which supported it. Although he was only a few days from turning fifteen, in contrast to Ethan, still shrouded in the cocoon of boyhood, Will's body was developing into the shape of a man's. Not only was Ethan proud of his brother's metamorphosis, but he was also a little envious. No bad feelings accompanied his envy though. The envy came with desire combined with the expectation for the time of his own metamorphosis. Ethan was eager to turn from a fledgling into a strong and graceful eagle.

Will felt his brother's gaze and turned toward him. His curls tossing the droplets of water that glistened in the sunlight. The handsome face broke into a smile and his eyes glossed with depth. Ethan coyly returned the smile and bowed his head. When he looked up again, Will already turned his back to him. He kept rowing.

The humming of the North Platte became clearer as they slowly approached it. To go down the river was the easy part. But to return the raft upstream was yet another story. At the end Will was exhausted and Ethan was so tired he wasn't sure if he still existed or not.

They pulled the raft ashore and fell onto the grass next to each other. Too weak for anything, but to take a rest, they fell asleep. Hoping that sleep would cure the pain in their aching muscles.

A few days passed before Ethan fully recovered. But, when the time came to embark upon new adventures, he didn't hesitate a moment. He jumped at his brother's call with no restraint and joined him to meet Derrick and Jason.

Derrick Zachariah and Jason Hawk were both Ethan's age. They were also his classmates and best friends. All three were good students and model boys. Although of a different social background, they got along rather well. Since they were all from Greenfield that was no big wonder.

Caught in the embrace of large and small ranches and farms reaching up to its suburbs and with its population about five thousand, many saw in Greenfield a typical American small town. Horses and cattle grazed on the bright, green pastures, and every bit of the fertile soil was well cultivated and planted with various crops. The Greenfielders were hardworking people. The foundation of their town—as they fondly called it—rested on their calluses and odor of the earth soaked with the sweat of their expectations.

Greenfield was smaller than Scottsbluff and Alliance—the nearby towns—as well as North Platte toward the east. Scottsbluff's population, for instance, exceeded Greenfield's by almost three times its number. While North Platte had almost twice as many people. However, to its residents, Greenfield was a town. The place founded by their grandfathers and the grandfathers of their fathers in blood, sweat, and self-sacrifice. Their sons contributed to its growth, and as would their sons' sons. For them, there was no other place they would rather take their first look upon the world, to work and enjoy the fruits of their hard labor, and—at the end—close their eyes and fall into their final sleep. Not only was Greenfield the ideal place to live, Greenfield was their paradise.

Ethan and Derrick were born Greenfielders, taught and brought up in the long tradition of love, candor, openness, and affability to everyone. That was why they readily accepted Jason, who moved from the West Coast six years ago. Bankruptcy and a spell of unfortunate circumstances drove his parents to move away and search for a new life elsewhere. They came across Greenfield, and it turned out to be their good luck. Because, if a man had to build everything anew, starting from a scratch, next to zero, Greenfield had all the preconditions to make something out of almost nothing. What most other American towns did partly, Greenfield did completely. It made the American dream come true.

Protestants, Catholics, Jews, Irish, Scots, Germans, French, Spaniards, Americans, the rich and the poor, the healthy and the sick; people of different colors, cultures, habits and political beliefs had overcome the differences that characterized them and the barriers that represented the insurmountable impediments in a less tolerable environment. Greenfield's residents forged a strong bond of acceptance and unity. Those bonds reached back to Ethan's and Derrick's great-grandfathers who, together with Weinbergs, Friedmans, Grays and Foures, were the founders of Greenfield. At that time, the American dream was just emerging, like the sails of a distant ship appearing on the horizon.

As it happens in life, when the wagon breaks loose and starts rolling down the hill, it is very difficult to stop it. The Hawks family learned that the hard way at their own expense. First, Jim Hawk lost his car wash due to his partner's bad luck at playing cards. A year later, his wife Gina also lost her job as a waitress in a fast-food restaurant that burned to the ground because of arson. If they hadn't been in a shock, they would have thought a lot about what possible reason anybody would have to set fire to a small, modest restaurant. Fortunately, it caused no heavy casualties. Gina suffered the only consequence when her lungs filled with smoke and lots of fear to overcome. These things happen in a modern world.

As Jim Hawk couldn't find a steady job and Gina was slowly recovering from what she had been through, they made up their minds to leave the coast and look for a new beginning inland. They took Jason—just five years and nine months at the time—with only the most necessary things and several hundred dollars of savings and set off. They stopped at many places, but with no real luck. The jobs they did find provided them with food and a shelter for a few days and then they had to set off again after a day or two. Their adopted son reached the age of six on one trip. When they had almost given up their last hope, they came across Greenfield. They didn't dare enjoy the beauty of the place, afraid the disappointment would be worse.

At the gas station Jim made inquiries whether there were any chances to get at least a temporary job in Greenfield. The attendant referred them to Benjamin Zachariah. He said Ben had just increased the number of the cattle he was raising and needed to hire extra workers. Jim Hawk didn't know a thing about cattle raising, but he thanked the attendant and went to find Benjamin Zachariah.

Jim Hawk was knocked off his feet when he met Ben. He received Jim as if he'd known him for years. It surprised Jim to learn that Benjamin Zachariah was a veterinarian by profession and that it was his main occupation. Raising cattle was an additional source of income, meant to provide a foundation for his children and get them off to a good start once they got on their own. Anyway, he didn't believe cattle raising would be the main occupation of his lifetime. After a short conversation, he offered Jim a job, even though Jim confessed he had no experience with animals. "I didn't have either," answered the veterinarian. "But I started. You'll learn. I can see you're an honest man, and it'd be a crazy thing to turn away a good and honest worker."

Jim Hawk, along with his wife and stepson, settled in at Ben Zachariah's farm. In addition to the house in the center of the small town in which he lived and also served as the hospital for his practice, Ben Zachariah owned several sheds on his ranch. The sheds had not been lived in (mainly the seasonal workers used them) and had decayed under the weather conditions. He welcomed someone who wanted to stay longer and live in them. The Hawks jumped at that offer with sincere gratitude.

Eight years later, when Ben Zachariah gave up cattle raising, Jim Hawk bought everything from him—all the animals including the ranch (with *his* house proudly standing on it now), and the pastures encircling it. The courtesy of Benjamin Zachariah made it possible for Jim Hawk to provide himself and his family a normal life again. It also restored their faith in the existence of good and honest people. And brought back joy to their life. But it was someone else Jim Hawk was grateful to for encouraging him to find the strength to negotiate his way out of the mud of humiliation, exploitation and discouragement. The love he felt for his stepson was his driving force. Jason was the one that gave the strength to Jim and Gina to strive, to keep up and not to yield. To keep on moving. They made it because of him.

So, the four friends—Will, Ethan, Jason, and Derrick—went out rafting. The boys were charged up even at the mere thought of going down the January River. When Derrick, Jason and Ethan found themselves on the raft, the excitement turned into euphoria. At that moment, trouble loomed. Unforeseen and unexpected, it hit them like a charging tornado.

Derrick's sister, Sarah, jumped out of the bushes growing on the riverbank. "Well, well! What do I see here?" She turned with a threatening tone to her several-minutes-older brother. His jaw almost fell to the raft and scraped on it as he couldn't believe his own eyes. "You didn't want to take me with you, did you? Did you think you could sneak out and run away just like that? Hasn't it occurred to you that your baby sister would like to come for a ride too?"

"What's that, for Christ's sake?" Jason whispered into Derrick's ear. "I thought you said everything's been taken care of with your sister. You were supposed to get *rid* of her."

"That was what I thought," moaned Derrick. "But it seems she tricked us again."

"Well, Der, what do you have to say in your defense?" She approached the water, showing no mercy at all.

"What the heck you brats think you're doin'?" Will stood in the water up to his knees, not knowing whether to climb on the raft or move toward Derrick's sister. "Haven't we agreed that just *four* of us were to go down the river?"

"We have, but it seems Derrick messed up," Jason commented helplessly.

"*I* messed up?! It cost me fifty cents!"

Will glanced at Ethan, who just shrugged his shoulders before staring at Sarah. "What do we do now?" He addressed his friends, although he looked at Sarah. "How do we solve this *situation*?" He stressed the word.

"We send home the uninvited party," Derrick said decisively, "and I mean right away! Or, I'm taking my fifty cents back."

"Oh no, my dearest and only brother. You won't get rid of me so easily. You lied! As you well know I can't stand lies, the price is now one dollar, not fifty cents! And I'll think it over whether to tell Mom and Dad where you have *really* been. They'll be so happy when they learn how shamelessly you lied to them."

"You little thief!" Derrick raised his voice. "Aren't you ashamed? What would Mom and Dad say if they knew what you are?"

"What would they say if they knew their son was a liar?" She brushed him off curtly and crossed her arms on her chest.

Derrick braced himself to jump off the raft, but Ethan stopped him.

"Knock it off, Der. It won't do any good. We may argue like that until the night falls and then wave goodbye to our rafting."

"I'm glad to see at least someone here has brains," Sarah

11

said, making no effort to hide her smile directed at Ethan, which made the boy feel uneasy.

"Hold it, guys," Will said.

The commotion on the raft ceased.

Having their attention, Will turned to Sarah. He looked at her as he would look at an equal and says in a reconciling manner, "Sarah, I'm sorry. But as you can see for yourself, your brother doesn't want you to come along. I'm afraid, nothing much can be done here. If you want the whole truth, neither do we want somebody else to come with us. The raft is too small and there isn't much space on it for another one. We could all capsize."

"It isn't the point that the raft is too small and that there isn't enough space for all of us. The point is, you don't want women with you."

"Oh no, we have nothing against women. Isn't that so, guys?" He winked at them. "But we have something against little girls who must be looked after all the time, if we don't want to lose them in one of the canals."

"I'm not a little girl," Sarah snorted. "Tell them, Der! I'm as good as you. You are not any better than me."

"Prove it," Jason said.

"That's it. Prove you are equal to us!" Ethan called out.

"Well?" Will asked, mimicking her posture, his hands crossed on his chest. "Have we agreed?"

"About what?"

"If you knock me down into the water," said Will, "you can climb on the raft and go with us. If I knock you down, you turn around and go home. Without whimpering, and you can keep your fifty cents."

Sarah knew that wasn't a fair offer. No twelve-year-old girl could be a match for a boy like Will, who was also two years older. She knew the odds were against her in this duel. But she also knew there was no alternative for her, but to accept it. It wasn't only the rafting at stake. Losing her honor and her pride were at risk too. She accepted the challenge.

She ran into the river and bumped into Will's opened arms.

His blue eyes met hers and his lips pulled into a smile as they approached hers, as if trying to sneak a kiss.

She opened her mouth and cried out as she sank, filling it with water.

Will kept hugging her while she coughed the water out, breathing in the tender smell of her freshly washed hair.

Then she pushed him away, looked firmly into his eyes, and turned away without saying a word.

"Wait." Will grabbed her by the arm. "Climb on. You deserve it."

She nodded a silent thank you and let him help her climb on the raft.

The boys moved to make her room. Will climbed on last. He winked at his brother, took the other oar and pushed the raft loose. It rolled gently and then drifted away.

The silence was interrupted only by the splashing of the oars and the hum of the water. Ethan stole a glance at his brother, his profile, the well-known face. He tried to make out what was the message in his look when he handed him his oar—something new, yet still familiar.

Then he remembered. The look Will gave him was the same look as when he gazed at Sarah's hair. It was also the look that Sarah shared with him, Ethan, making him feel strange. That was for Ethan a new, hitherto unknown, apprehensive feeling.

Everything might have been just his imagination. Which was also drifting away as their little adventure was coming to its end.

3

Sarah Zachariah. And her brother Derrick.

He hadn't seen her for a long time. Far too long. Although he visited Greenfield, two years ago, their paths hadn't crossed. Ten years before that, he was driving his Rover through the center of Greenfield on the way out. And then he spotted her. She was leaving the school building with a crowd of children around her. She stared at the unknown car as it passed her, and their eyes met. They both nodded their heads in recognition.

As the car swerved around the corner and drove down the next street, Sarah still looked after it. Her face was expressionless, her eyes motionless. Several tufts of her dark, red hair escaped from her carefully made bun. The strands shook disobediently in the wind. She held a little girl by the hand.

The Sarah he spotted in that fraction of time—as short and transient as a sigh, but long enough to leave an imprint on his memory—was another Sarah. Not the same as the girl he knew in his childhood. Different and strange, but then, again, still close. He recognized her at once. And he saw that longing, nostalgic look in her eyes—but also a decisive one.

The woman looking at him from the schoolyard clutching

the little girl's hand was beautiful. The dark-blue, straight dress, taken in around the waist, touched her knees, discreetly revealing the figure hidden beneath it. The red hair framing her tender, straight face glittered in the sunset—taking on a wild, fiery shine with each movement of her head. Her dark eyes radiated warmth, but also hinted at a trace of sorrow. When he met her look, Ethan had to avert his eyes.

When their gazes met again, it was as if it were many years ago in their childhood. Her eyes burned with some dangerous, untamed wildness. Challenging, cheeky and provoking, they scrutinized the world around them. The strength they exuded somehow came from that small, bony and frail body. That plain and slender girl who stood before him had long arms and legs, and garish, orange hair. Her freckled face invited the boys to tease and, thus, provoke her. Straight as a plank of wood, with an oversized nose and an intelligent look, she was always ready to put up a fight whenever her brother became the laughing stock of the school or was subjected to ridicule. Many times, she fought stronger and tougher boys, assaulting them with both her hands and legs, sparing neither herself nor them. She punched them with her fists, plucked their hair, bit them to the point of bleeding—all to defend her brother and protect the Zachariahs' honor.

On one occasion she tossed a chair at Warren Preston, hitting his head. The skin broke at the place of impact and Warren's head started bleeding. The schoolmaster summoned her which resulted in a reprimand and suspension from school for a day. The interview with the parents followed. She didn't even try to explain to them she was defending the Zachariahs' honor. They wouldn't understand, anyway. Derrick, who always stood aside whenever she fought his fights for him, didn't understand her either. He was too scared and too weak to do anything to help her. He always shrank into a corner trying to get as far away as possible from all the others. The thick lenses of his glasses and the locks of his shaggy hair falling over them conveniently hid his misty eyes brimming with tears. His plump body and belly shook and shivered as he sobbed.

Unlike Sarah, who used to take matters into her own hands, Derrick didn't know how to fight the injustice. He always suffered the humiliation and insults, praying to Adonai to give mercy and rescue him. But Sarah always rescued him. Sarah took the consequences without complaint. She was her brother's keeper. To her, nothing had ever been too hard to do for him. Not when her parents grounded her to the house, a punishment they imposed to make her toe the discipline line. Or any other restriction when she crossed the line of what they considered acceptable. Whenever Derrick's well-being was in question, she took any and all of the knocks that came her way.

Sarah loved her brother. And Derrick loved Sarah. (How could he not after all she had done for him?) Inside his clumsy, and to some extent ridiculous, body, there was a good heart. In moments when he was alone with his sister, or when they were surrounded with the people they loved, felt accepted and safe, his heart was filled with peace and contentment instead of fear and glowed with its full magnitude and strength. Then it loved, then it was the real Derrick. Derrick Zachariah.

Mulling over Sarah and her brother, Ethan couldn't help thinking once more of Will and himself. He felt again that miraculous bond of love that connected them just as it had been between Sarah and Derrick. Ethan had never been mocked like Derrick, but that didn't mean he was immune to incidents and improprieties happening to him like any other child. That was part of growing up. In such situations, Will always intervened on his brother's behalf. He stood up for him, encouraging him and even lied for him. For William Patrick McCoy it had never been a problem to invent an innocuous lie to his own father if it might save his younger brother. He never had to lie to his mother. She had such a good heart and a nice temperament. She never punished him after an open confession.

Her husband, Sean McCoy, though, never spared the cane if he felt he had to prove to his sons their wrongdoings. Such occasions were rare, but when it came to that, everything was more for show than a real wish to teach the young McCoys a lesson by a physical punishment.

Sean McCoy preferred the conversation. The upbringing by his father, Patrick McCoy, after whom Will was named too, had implanted in him the view that nothing could bring better results than an open, straight discussion. He thought such an approach brought peace to the house, but it also fostered the bond of trust and respect indispensable for any family to live in harmony. And when the respect and order existed in one's own family, others would respect that family too.

Patrick McCoy accomplished that. The McCoys were respected in the eyes of the inhabitants of Greenfield. Not only because of their wealth, for they owned a general store, fields with wheat and barley crops, a mill which turned all the crops of the region into flour that was transported in big sacks to Scottsbluff and further on, plus a twenty-percent stockholding in the local bank which inspired awe in their fellow townsmen. No. Patrick McCoy had given a great contribution to the benefit of Greenfield and for his townsmen with his wisdom, diligence and hard work. He passed the values he inherited from his father Robert to his son Sean, thus continuing the tradition.

Sean McCoy and Benjamin Zachariah, together with Martin Friedman, Elliot Gray and Norman Foure, were the backbone of today's Greenfield as their fathers had been the same in the past. They were all credited for Greenfield having become what it was today. They all rose above their individual differences whenever the interests of their town were at stake, and they invested their money, used their influence and rolled up their sleeves whenever it became necessary. Inspired by the examples they've set, their fellow townsmen followed them readily and voluntarily.

Although made up of a community of imperfect, ordinary people, with their good qualities and weaknesses, successes and failures, loves and sorrows, hopes and desperation, Greenfield functioned perfectly as an entity. Those used to a life full of actions and everyday excitements such as robberies, killings and the smell of terror, would find Greenfield with its harmony and a steady way of life boring and even illusory. Ethan McCoy knew best that beneath that harmony, Greenfield wasn't boring at all, that its inhabitants had their internal traumas, pains and perturbations and that they too had to put up with small tragedies of their own. Ethan McCoy knew the inhabitants of Greenfield were ordinary people. He was also aware of their vulnerability and mortality.

4

Ethan McCoy differed from his friends of the same age by a sensibility of his soul and his outstanding sense for beauty. While his friends spent the better part of their free time at basketball, baseball or football games—either playing them by themselves or watching them on TV—Ethan took his bicycle and pedaled out into the countryside. He enjoyed evening rides the most. As the air became cooler and more pleasant, the sweltering heat and stuffiness of the day retreated into the advancing night. He pumped the pedals of his BMX, jumping over potholes in the woods' path, always dashing for a clearing surrounded by the crowns of the evergreens and deciduous trees.

Hopping off the bicycle, he let it fall onto the tall grass woven with various wildflowers. Spreading out his hands, he raised his head toward the night watchers' crowned tops. Ethan filled his lungs with the scent of the woods blended with the fragrance of dog-violets, columbines, larkspurs and wild roses—feeling the environment's pulse. His bloodstream synchronized with the stream of fluids of the woods, he sensed every hum, every movement, every rustle of a leaf. Enchanted, he cried out into the night. The cry of wilderness, the cry of nature.

The cry of ecstasy.

Dizzy, he sat down on the trunk of a cottonwood tree and gazed down at Greenfield below him. As night fell, the houses lit up, followed by the street lamps decorating the little town with thousands of glowing lights. The night sky, spangled with stars, seemed to have found its own reflection. In the far distance, behind the hills, the pastures and the woods, the sun set, its last rays of light painting the clear sky with pastel colors.

Ethan loved sunsets most of all. Whenever he could, after his parents released him from household chores, he disappeared to that clearing. He enjoyed watching the sunsets appearing every evening, but never the same. No matter how often the sun rose and set, each unique sunset brought a new fascination and grace to their town. But what Ethan saw that evening made him wince, sending creepy shivers all through his body.

The forest calling him from the distance was now indigo as if someone brushed it with a coat of black ink, or something swallowed it leaving the habitat in a dark pit. The orange complexion of the sky developed a dark-reddish tint, turning it blue. As the sun sank behind the horizon, the rainbow of colors spilled over the sky. The deep-red color ran along the brink of the forest, with lilac and blue above it disappearing into the far distance. The last of the rays radiated intense yellow embroidered by threads of orange. To Ethan, that light resembled the color of lava in the midst of its swell. Descending from the sky and swallowing up everything in its path—the forest, himself, and the spectacular phenomenon. Just when he thought his excitement had reached its climax, an extraordinary thing happened. Something that made him recoil and almost fall off the trunk of the cottonwood tree on which he sat.

A streak of lightning flashed through the palette of colors and light in the night. A greenish glow spread over the last. tiny part of the illuminated sky. And the sun sank below the horizon. The time of the night marched on. Ethan choked, coughed, his guts shivering.

He jumped to his feet and stumbled. As if he were drunk.

Spellbound, still looking at the sky, he tottered toward his bicycle. Stumbling upon it, he lost his balance and fell, bruising his knee. He picked himself up as fast as he could and, shivering all over, mounted the bicycle. Missing the pedal, he shot forward and almost fell again. Struggling to keep upright while his bicycle jumped and yawed like a wild mustang, he sped toward Greenfield quick as greased lightning.

Willy! I've got to find Willy, he thought feverishly while the cold, night air whipped his face.

Will lay in semi-darkness when Ethan burst headlong into his room. The last chords of "What a Wonderful World" came from the radio. Ethan stopped at the door for a moment, waiting for Will's reaction for invading his privacy without knocking. Nothing happened. In the soft light, Will remained motionless as if he were dead, though his chest moved up and down. Otis Redding's "(Sittin' On) The Dock of the Bay" replaced Louis Armstrong on the radio.

Ethan felt as if he himself were on some dock of the bay because Will's room had that kind of feel. The blue walls splashed with waves in all shades of an angry sea. Posters of *Titanic* and the sailboat *Dauphine* hung above his bed, with the picture of the steamship *Alexander Hamilton* over his desk. Ethan felt as if he was in the middle of an ocean. In a realm surrounded by water and ships.

Before he got seasick, he came to his brother's bed and shook him. "Willy, wake up," he called, trying to be considerate and gentle.

Will muttered something and, turning over on his side, continued sleeping.

"Willy, Willy," Ethan tried again, now more energetically. "Wake up!"

"Hmmm, what happened?" Will said, still half-asleep. "Supper ready?"

"No, it's not, but you must wake up."

"What is it? Something happened?"

"You won't believe it when I tell you. You won't believe it," Ethan shook his head as he spoke.

"What won't I believe?" Will now sat up in his bed, fully awaken. "Don't tell me you did it again."

"Yes. Well, I mean no. You must swear you won't tell anybody if I tell you."

"Okay, I'm listening."

"Swear?"

"God almighty, cross my heart and hope to die, I won't tell anyone. Satisfied now?"

Ethan licked his lips and nodded his head three times. "I've just returned from the grove. I watched the sunset, like I usually do, and then it happened."

"What happened?"

Ethan took a breath, put his hand upon his brother's shoulder and clutched it. "The aliens. I've seen the aliens!"

"What?" Will gaped at him with a blank look.

"I saw the aliens land!"

"Where? Where did they land?"

"In the woods. Behind Marvin's pastures."

"Is this a joke?"

"No. I swear, I saw them."

"You saw them landing in the Marvin's woods."

"Yes. The green light flashed in the sky and then disappeared behind the woods. They must have landed there."

"And you saw it all—"

"From the usual place."

"From your usual place."

"Right. In the clearing where I always watch sunsets."

"Was anyone with you? I mean, did anybody else see the aliens besides you?"

"No. I was alone. . . . Just me. . . . Willy, you don't believe me?"

"Listen, Et. Is there any chance everything you saw was an

illusion?"

"No!"

"You know how carried away with the nature stuff you can get. Maybe you saw something else and mistook it for aliens. . . ."

"It was not an illusion! It really happened."

After Otis Redding, commercials came on, followed by Tina Turner's "River Deep, Mountain High."

"Aliens in Greenfield? Et, what would they do here? Think about that. Wouldn't they choose some other, more interesting place to land?"

"How should *I* know? I'm telling you what I saw."

Their mother's voice came from downstairs, calling for supper.

"All right, here's what we'll do. We go down for supper now, and tomorrow we'll go together to the Marvin's woods to check if anything unusual has happened there. Is that okay with you?"

"Will, tomorrow may be late. They might leave by tomorrow. They may sneak us out at night and take us hostage. We must go *tonight*. Right after supper."

"And what are we gonna tell our parents? Where are we going to at this time of the night? Rafting? Or maybe alien hunting?"

"We won't tell them anything. Nothing until we have collected the evidence. They wouldn't believe a word."

"Ethan! Will! Supper is on the table," their mother called again.

"Coming," Will called back, sliding off the bed. He turned to Ethan. "We'll take care of everything tomorrow. Don't you worry."

"But tomorrow—"

"Et," Will interrupted him in mid-sentence. "Bumping into blood-thirsty aliens in the middle of the night, darkness, woods, alone and unarmed. . . . Sorry, bro, it doesn't seem appealing to me. How about you?"

"Uh, I. . . ."

"Come on, let's go down for supper." He embraced his brother around his shoulders and shoved him out of the room.

The Beach Boys sang "God Only Knows."

After saying grace, their father read several lines from the Bible before the food was brought to the table. That was a family service in the McCoys' home, which also had its roots in the tradition reaching back to Sean's great-grandfather.

Supper passed in silence. Their mother and father exchanged a few words, with father as usual praising the well-made meal, while Will and Ethan exchanged meaningful glances. At one moment Will came to the point of bursting out laughing and thus sprinkling his brother sitting across the table with his half-swallowed soup. He barely pulled himself together and made it possible for their supper to end in peace.

Upstairs again, as they got ready for bed, Will left the bathroom and stopped for a moment outside Ethan's doorway. With the door opened wide, Ethan knelt beside his bed praying. Will waited for him to finish, and then whispered: "Hey, bro?"

Startled, Ethan turned around.

"Sweet dreams!" Will winked.

Ethan nodded solemnly. "See you in the morning."

"You bet," Will moved toward his room, grinning.

He left the door to his room opened. He wanted to be at hand in case his baby brother encountered the aliens in his dreams.

5

That night Ethan didn't sleep well—he barely closed his eyes. When dawn broke and the first rays of the sun appeared, he was already afoot. Fresh and eager for the alien hunt. He sneaked into his brother's room and shook him.

"Willy, Willy, wake up! Wake up, we have to go!"

"Mmm. . . ."

"W-i-l-l-y!" Ethan's voice resembled the quiet whine of a wounded coyote pup captured in a deadly snare.

"What is it!?"

"We must go! The aliens, remember?" he whispered into Will's ear.

Will yawned and squinted at him. "What time is it?"

"It's past five."

"Five? You're waking me up at five o'clock in the morning?" Willy couldn't believe his ears.

"But we must go—"

"We must go nowhere. It's Sunday. Let me sleep."

"But, the aliens. . . ." Ethan was getting desperate, watching his brother's indifference to their important mission.

"What aliens?"

"The aliens that landed in Marvin's woods yesterday. Don't

you *remember*? We talked about it last night," Ethan said, anger rising in his voice.

"Ah yes, the aliens," Will said, only half-awake.

"Will, get up, please."

"Forget it. I'm sleepy. Besides, it's Sunday."

"But you *promised*! You promised we would go look for the aliens! You can't. . . ."

"Ethan, listen to me. If there were any aliens, they'd be gone by now. If they're still alive, they've probably already left. If not, we'll find them later, anyway. They won't run away. Now, be a good boy and go back to your bed."

"No! You promised me. You promised to come with me right away in the morning."

"I did. But I said nothing about *when* in the morning. I want to sleep now, so will you please leave me alone for an hour or two? We'll go hunting your aliens later."

"Later, you'll go alone," Ethan spat out. He marched out of Will's room, barely controlling himself not to slam the door behind him.

Will buried his face in the pillow and the next minute he was sound asleep again.

Ethan showered and dressed in haste. He found a rope, took a hunting knife and a battery (not that he knew what he would do with it if he bumped into the aliens), a sandwich with some fruits, and tucked them in a backpack. He sneaked out of the house on his toes, without making a sound.

From the garage, he pulled out his BMX, mounted it and sped down the street.

The small town looked deserted for a Sunday morning. Not a soul on the streets, even the dogs and the cats hid somewhere, sleeping.

No cars or acquaintances to say "Hi" and slow him down. He was satisfied with his quick progress.

Ethan passed the Presbyterian Church he attended every week with the rest of his family. He turned onto the field path by the graveyard, leaving behind small clouds of dust as he rode away. Wheat and corn fields were on both sides of the path, with canes standing up as still as the soldiers holding a guard. No wind, no sound—only a lonely rooster crowing from time to time in the distance.

Leaving behind the pastures and grass fields from which the rabbits leapt crossing his path, he reached his destination. He leaned the bicycle against the wild plum tree that grew in a group of three at the beginning of the woods which he could use as a reference point. Partially covered with low shrubs, they would be hard to spot by anyone coming from the same direction he had.

With the backpack loosely strapped on his back, a rope tied around his waist and a firm grip on the knife in his hand, he entered the woods.

His heart beat faster when something stirred in the bush he passed, and he was overcome by a cold sweat. A young opossum jumped out of the blueberry bush and ran away. Realizing he was in no danger, Ethan laughed with relief at his exaggerated fear. Encouraged, he moved on.

Although alert with every step, he couldn't ignore the beauty of the woods he roamed. The suspense edged away as he watched the sky through the crowns of the trees filtering the rare sun rays. Unfamiliar small plants, grass, and flowers grew in deep shadows of the huge trees. Ethan enjoyed watching the acrobatic squirrels as they jumped from branch to branch, especially thrilled to see a pair of playful raccoons. He almost forgot about the aliens. Unafraid of them now, he thought of a possible encounter as some science-fiction story rather than a personal experience.

Unsure how long or far he'd walked, he felt hungry. He guessed not more than half an hour, but since he left his watch at home in a hurry, there was no way of knowing the time. Besides, in his excitement he hadn't eaten much supper last night.

Thus, it came as no surprise that his stomach growled at him this early.

Ethan lowered himself onto a root of a big oak tree projecting from the ground and took the first apple from his backpack. Savoring its juice, he rested his eyes on the surrounding greenery alive with a rich variety of sounds.

The forest was waking up. And Greenfield would too, soon.

He finished the second apple and then got on the move again. Out of habit, he still had the knife in his hand. He didn't believe anymore that he'd have to use it. And it wouldn't be of much use to him anyway should he have to defend himself against bloodthirsty visitors from outer space. As he penetrated the deep woods further, he thought he heard church bells ring. Not time for mass yet, Ethan couldn't figure out why the bells rang. Soon the ringing stopped. And Ethan believed it had only been his imagination, likely prompted as a warning against going too far out and getting lost. Though Marvin's woods were not a large forest, it was unknown to Ethan. Meaning that finding his bicycle again could turn into a little adventure of its own.

Ethan stopped, hesitating as he considered whether to carry on or turn around and go back. With no trace of aliens, he wondered whether there would be any—which he doubted. The time for mass approached, and he had planned to be back home by then. The reason he had set out so early. Also, it would save him a lot of explaining to his parents.

The call of the woods stronger, Ethan decided to search for ten more minutes. If nothing unusual happened, he'd turn around.

His stomach reminded him of its existence, once more craving food. Ethan took off the backpack and dug into it for the sandwich. This time he didn't stop, but ate while walking. The trees in the woods grew sparser, and the sun penetrated through their crowns with more vigor. The wildflowers and the shrubs gave way to larger bushes and smaller trees, and it dawned on Ethan that he approached the end of the woods. He realized he'd walked through almost the full width of the woods without finding any trace of the aliens. He'd known the hunt would not be easy. He also knew something else, and that thought upset him.

Will was right.

Everything was just an illusion.

The aliens were only in his mind.

He would die of shame and mockery, become the laughing stock of Greenfield. He must stop Will as soon as possible before he babbled to somebody.

Ethan ran back as fast as his legs could carry him. He ran into bushes, fell into holes, and stumbled over protruding roots. He got lost several times and had to go back. Soaked in sweat, gasping for air, he still went on. He had to get home *now*. He forgot about mass. His only concern was to prevent becoming a disgrace and embarrassment to his family.

The fear crept into him, followed by panic. What if he were just going around in circles? What if he couldn't find the way out? What if the day faded into evening trapping him in the woods? And then the blackness of night engulfed him? What if his parents organized a search party? Greenfield would buzz the next morning. Oh God, oh God, be merciful on him.

He leaned against a tree and slid down to take a little rest. Mad at his foolishness for not taking along at least some water. He was *so* thirsty. What if he died of dehydration? What if the coyotes pulled his small, exhausted body apart? Bit off his nose and ate out his eyes?! No, he mustn't think of that. He had to see things in a positive light. He had to think about nice things. He had to think about . . . apples.

He cried with joy as he spotted the remnants of the apples he ate a short while ago. He cupped them into his hands to feel them, to make sure they were real, that he wasn't hallucinating. They were real.

He was on the right track. He hadn't gotten lost.

He threw the remnants of the apples with a small army of ants crawling on them away and moved off. His legs ached and his breathing heavy, but he didn't want to give up. Just a little more and he would be out of the woods safe and sound. He pictured himself jumping on his bicycle, riding away faster than he ever rode before, and arriving home before his parents got worried once they learned the truth from Will.

He shielded his eyes with his hand as he ran into the blinding sunshine. Ethan thought the temperature had risen at least thirty degrees since he went into the woods. He looked down at his T-shirt glued to his skin with perspiration, examined his pants, his dirty socks and scraped legs. He didn't remember when or how he got scraped. Never mind, he'd come up with a story on his way home. Maybe say he fell off his bicycle or something. When he found his bicycle, none of that mattered anymore. He dragged it out of the shrubs and jumped on it. The pain cut into his leg muscles. His legs were stiff as if made of steel. His muscles hurt. He pedaled slowly until he got accustomed to the motion again. He didn't expect the return home to be so hard, or that things would work out this way. With fear, he worried what might be in store for him as he pedaled faster and faster.

He threw the bicycle to the ground in front of the garage and left it lying there. He ran toward the rear of the house and entered the kitchen, where he stopped in his tracks. Staring at the kitchen clock, he couldn't believe his eyes.

Two o'clock in the afternoon.

The time for mass had come and gone long ago. And the same for lunch.

No, it can't be!

His mother held a dishtowel in her hand, tidying up the remains of the finished meal. The smell of food disappeared through the wide-open porch door. She spotted Ethan, stopped in half movement and opened her mouth as if she were about to say something. She didn't utter a sound. The concern was still painted all over her face, but there were also bright traces of relief in the corners of her mouth.

"Mother, I. . . ." Ethan didn't know what words to use to express his sorrow.

Ira McCoy put away the kitchen cloth and moved toward her son. "I. . . ."

Ethan took a step toward her and ran into her embrace.

She kissed his shaggy hair while he shivered in her arms. After a few moments, she pushed him away and said: "Your father is waiting for you in his study. He would like to talk to you." Her voice was gentle, but hoarse from unshed tears.

She wiped his tears and said, "Go now."

Sean McCoy sat behind his massive oak desk, rummaging through a heap of paper lying in front of him. A pipe hung between his lips, spreading a sweet scent.

It didn't matter to him it was Sunday. The word *rest* never existed in Sean McCoy's vocabulary. While most of his fellow townsmen used it to enjoy the fruits of their hard work and a deserved rest, Sean McCoy's policy was that something could always be done or improved upon. He always did his best to act according to his life motto. Rarely, if ever, had Sean McCoy left anything unfinished or half done.

A hardworking man, Sean McCoy sometimes was even too harsh on himself. He had an inexhaustible source of energy he put to good use. He was one of those people who needed little or almost no rest.

He cleared away the papers he worked on, blew off a few cloudlets of fine smoke and looked at his son. Ethan struck a pose of someone who had just been arrested after attempting to escape and then forcefully returned to the crime scene.

Shifting his weight from one leg to the other and hiding his jumpiness by putting his hands behind his back, Ethan spoke up. "Good afternoon, Father. Mother said you wanted to talk."

His father kept looking at him, stroking his thick beard.

Ethan breathed deeply. Insecurity emanated from every pore. He looked through his father, through the window behind his back, into the distance.

"Do you know why I wanted to talk to you?" his father asked, after several, painfully, long minutes.

"I do," Ethan squeezed out in a feeble voice. Lowering his head, he couldn't find the courage to meet his father's look.

"That means you realize what you've done and the effect it has had upon your mother and me?"

"Yes, sir."

"I won't tell you it must not happen again because I'm sure you know it won't happen again."

Ethan didn't know whether that was an assertion or his father expected an answer from him, so he nodded just to be on the safe side.

"From now on, every time you leave the house you are to tell your mother or me where you are going and when you will be coming home. Is that understood?"

"Yes, Father," Ethan was relieved. He could hardly believe he got away that easily. He tried to smile, but it was a poor smile resembling a grin.

"Are you hungry?" his father asked.

Ethan's heart raced—not only was he dying for a warm meal, but he was thirsty too. Still, he lied and said: "No, thank you. I'm not hungry."

"Good. Because you won't get anything. Your meals are denied to you for today."

Ethan stood as if struck by lightning.

"If you have nothing more to say, you can retire to your room. I believe you are writing an essay on history on Tuesday, so you will need time to prepare it. Use it wisely, son."

"Yes, sir," Ethan whispered and moved toward the door. "Understood, sir."

His father's voice stopped him. "Ethan McCoy."

"Yes, Father?"

"Maybe you don't understand now, but you will understand one day it's for your own good. You'll understand when you have children of your own." He confirmed his words with the nod of his head, waving to Ethan permission to leave.

Ethan drove his fingernails hard into his palms. Blinking the tears away, he addressed his father: "I understand, Father. I think I understand now."

And ran to his room.

He hadn't spotted a thin smile, as delicate as a puff of smoke, which flickered for a short moment on his father's face.

Seconds later, somebody knocked at the door to his room. Ethan jumped from his bed to sit at the table. Switching on the light as fast as he could, he buried his head into the papers, pretending to study.

Pitch dark outside, Ethan knew he had missed the sunset. Though painful to put up with, the hunger pangs he felt in his empty stomach were worse. Even tougher and stronger boys than Ethan couldn't get through a day on one sandwich and two apples. Therefore, it came as no big surprise that his brain wasn't taking in the new data. Meanwhile, stuff he already learned got messed up, resulting in considerable confusion in his head.

Will stood at the door. Ethan breathed a sigh of relief when he saw him, but then remembered Will was in part to blame for his situation. He answered his brother's question, "How are you?" with a frown.

After he received no answer, Will said, "What are you learning?"

Silence.

"Listen, Et, I know you're mad at me, and you have every reason to be. But I came to apologize and make it up with you."

Ethan's throat grew dry. He wanted to embrace his brother and say: *Yes, Willy, I want to make up with you too. I'm not mad anymore. I want us to be friends again.* But his pride stopped him.

"I'd like you to forgive me. I know how you feel. . . ."

"You know?" The tone of Ethan's voice sounded fiercer than he intended. "Do you? Do you know what it's like to go hungry all day? What it's like to be closed in a room for the entire afternoon to learn, while the only thing going around in your head is food, food and yet again FOOD? Do you know what it's like when you have to force your brain to memorize stupid dates and numbers when you are exhausted and overwhelmed? Do you know that feeling, big brother?"

"I do . . . well, I don't. That's why I came. Dad sent me to fetch you for supper."

Ethan couldn't believe what he just heard. When Will's words registered, nothing could hold back his tears.

"It's all right, Et." Will patted his back. "Everything's okay."

"How come . . . how come he changed his mind?" he muttered through his sobs.

"I talked to him and explained what happened. Should have told him when we realized you wouldn't be back for the mass, but . . . I was afraid. I didn't know what to say. Frankly, I didn't think you would miss both lunch and supper. When Mum told me that, I knew I had to do something. I'm to blame too. I told Dad, you were planning to go to the Marvin's woods. . . ."

Ethan's eyes widened, fearing what else Will might have said, but it turned out William Patrick was his usual cunning and quick-witted self.

"I told him you saw stags near those woods and you wanted to take a closer look. I failed to mention it right away because I didn't consider it important. Besides, I also figured you'd be back soon. I worried only when you didn't turn up for lunch.

"I also pointed out to him you hadn't left without telling anyone, because I knew. The problem was, I didn't tell when I ought to. I admitted my mistake to him."

"And . . . did he accept your apology?"

"Yes and no. He pondered for a long time without saying a word. I suspected he'd be true to himself this time and push it right through to the end. That's why I took advantage of his silence and added it was pointless to deny you supper too. Because we both were guilty. You'd been denied lunch, which I had eaten. So, I should skip supper to work off my share of the guilt. I also asked him not to punish you for what I'd done because I knew I wouldn't be able to look into your eyes ever again."

"And?" Ethan's suspense was building up. "What did he say?"

"His pipe dropped out of his mouth and he roared with laughter," Will laughed. "You wouldn't be able to look into his eyes ever again, he repeated after me as he laughed, so I laughed too. What else could I do? Then he sent me to fetch you, warning us we'd better not think of doing anything like that ever again."

Ethan stared wide-eyed. "Do you think he believed your story? Do you think he won't be checking on us anymore? I would die if he learned about the aliens."

"I don't know if he believed it, but he forgave us. That's what counts most, right? That he forgave us and that you can fill your stomach now."

"Guess you're right. Thank you, Willy. I don't know what I would—"

"Oh, cut the crap! That's why we have each other. I did nothing you wouldn't do for me if you were in my shoes. Let's go down to supper now, before Dad changes his mind."

"Yeah, we better do that." Ethan stood up, trying to suppress the rumbling in his stomach as it woke up again at the thought of food.

"I say, Et, let me ask you something before we go down?" Will put his arm around his brother's thin shoulders.

"Go ahead."

"Did you find any aliens in the woods?"

Ethan blushed, his ears turning crimson red. He tore apart from his brother's hug and, whipping him with a stern look, sped downstairs.

Will followed him choking with laughter.

"We are grateful to Thee, Lord, for the mercy which we found and enjoy in Thy eyes. We thank Thee for Thy protection and all the gifts and the kindness which Thee bestow upon us every day. Thank Thee for blessing this family and for the life of peace we enjoy, and for this food before us which we shall take in our thankfulness and remembrance of Thee. Accept this grace in the name of Jesus. Amen."

"Amen," repeated Ira McCoy, Will and Ethan in one voice when Sean McCoy had finished the grace.

Sean McCoy then took the Bible, opened to the Gospel according to Luke and looked at each member of his family gathered around the table. His glance stopped at his younger son as he turned to him, saying in a pleasant baritone, "Ethan, can we ask you to read something from the Bible for us?"

Ethan's jaw dropped in surprise. Will and his mother were no less startled. They stared in disbelief at father, and then at Ethan, who was gulping air.

In the McCoy family, the custom had always been that the father, as head of the family, read the scriptures. Tension hung thick in the air at breaking the longstanding tradition. Something significant was happening. Everything lay in Ethan's hands now.

"Ethan?" his father called. "We're waiting for your answer."

"Well . . . I. . . ." Uneasy and a little scared, Ethan looked around.

Sean McCoy waited, observing his son with tranquil eyes.

"Well, I guess it's all right with me if the rest of you agree," Ethan muttered.

His father handed him the Bible. "Please, read Luke, second chapter, from the 41st to the 52nd verse."

Ethan took the Bible from him and glanced over the lines before beginning. He trembled when he saw some lines underlined. He knew only too well they had not been highlighted by chance. His father did nothing by accident. Ethan also knew he hadn't called attention to them only to emphasize their meaning.

Ethan knew the words referred to him, conveying a secret message intended for him alone. His father wanted to tell him something, and he would do it through verses from the Bible.

Those words spoke of the magnitude of love his father felt for him. Of his worries and trepidation with which he followed his son's growing up, but also the pride he felt in Ethan's maturing and progressing in his wisdom. Now it became clear to Ethan why his father chose him (and not Will) to read from the Bible. He understood what his father was asking him to do and what an honor he bestowed upon him. But he also recognized the responsibility that came with it.

Ethan cleared his throat and, in spite of his trembling, read about the twelve-year-old Jesus who stayed behind in Jerusalem where he went with his parents at the feast of the Passover. His concerned parents went a day's journey supposing he had been in their company before they turned back again to Jerusalem and found him in the temple where he sat with doctors hearing them with astonishing understanding and asking them questions.

Ethan paused and tossed a quick glance at his father who watched him without batting an eyelid. The blood flushed into his cheeks as he read on about how Jesus' parents were amazed by him even though they didn't understand what he was saying. They took Jesus to Nazareth with them where he increased in wisdom and stature in favor with God and every man.

Ethan stared at the lines he had just read and closed the Bible. He looked at his father with his eyes full of tears and whispered, "I'm sorry. . . . I'm so sorry."

Sean McCoy nodded and asked his wife to serve supper.

Ira McCoy took the Bible from Ethan and stroked his head.

Tears rolled down Ethan's cheeks.

Sean McCoy put a linen napkin over his lap while the supper steamed in his plate.

Joking, Will hit his brother with his leg under the table.

Ethan looked at him with eyes gleaming with tears.

Will then smiled at him and winked as a cool cat would.

Ethan laughed and wiped the tears away.

He reached for the bowl of soup.

6

Ethan didn't want to discuss the unsuccessful search for aliens with anyone, not even his best friends, Jason and Derrick. His brother William Patrick was the only one who knew about that shame. Ethan prayed to God for everything to stay that way and his brother not to blab the secret out to someone. In that case, he would have to flee from Greenfield and move as far away as possible. Everybody would mock him. The life he knew in his hometown would be finished for him.

Classes were over for today and he was just leaving the school with Jason and Derrick when he heard Sarah calling him. Sensing the looming troubles, Jason and Derrick left in a haste wishing their friend good luck. They had barely parted when Sarah was beside him.

"Hi," she greeted him. "How did the test go?" She was cheerful, too cheerful in Ethan's opinion.

"It was all right. How about you? How did you write it?" he asked, more out of courtesy than a real interest.

"I'm quite satisfied. I could even get an A or B, provided Custer was merciful."

"Custer" was their history professor's nickname. He was famous for his bloodthirstiness and rigor toward his students, which weren't much behind Custer's cruelty toward the North American Indians. That's how he earned that nickname.

"Actually, I needed you about something else. Wanted to ask you, what were you doing on Saturday night?"

Ethan grew even more suspicious, becoming alert.

"I was at the clearing above Greenfield watching the sunset. Why are you asking?"

"And?" Sarah asked, as if she had given him a difficult riddle.

"And what?"

"How did you like it?"

"Like what?"

"The sunset, silly!"

"It was fantastic," Ethan said with candor.

"And that's all?"

"What do you mean?"

"You haven't seen anything?"

Ethan's heart beat faster. If Will had given the game away, he would wring his neck, regardless of the consequences.

"I don't know what you mean?" Ethan pretended to be disinterested.

"Haven't you seen something veeery unusual?" Sarah said, her eyes aflame. "That's a pity. Something like that happens on a very, very, rare occasion!"

"So, you saw something?" Ethan wasn't disinterested anymore, his heart pumping faster and faster in his chest.

"Oh yes, you bet I did!" Sarah said roguishly. "Wasn't it *exciting*?"

"And I thought I was the only one who saw them! How could I have been so stupid! I should have known somebody else must have seen them too."

"Who do you mean?" Now, it was Sarah's turn to look confused.

"The aliens!" Ethan shouted, getting carried away. He saw a bewildered expression on her face and bit his lip, cursing his rashness.

"The aliens?"

"Well, yes. Weren't we talking about them?" he tried to save the situation.

"I don't know what you were talking about, but I was talking about the *green flash*." Then, she added, as if suddenly remembering, *"Aliens?"*

"The green flash?" It was Ethan's turn again to be astonished. He was so puzzled that he didn't hear her question.

"Yes. The wonderful, green light which appeared in the sky before the sun set."

"But that's what I was talking about!"

Sarah paused for a moment, and then said in a serious tone, "But, Et, that wasn't the aliens!"

Ethan kept quiet for fear of making an even bigger fool of himself.

"The green light resulted from an interaction between the sun's light and the earth's atmosphere."

Ethan looked at Sarah as if she had just dropped from Mars. *Sarah the Alien.* Perhaps they abducted her during the night and made her one of their own. They may lurk somewhere now, waiting for her to finish what they had begun, which meant the complete town of Greenfield now brimmed with Martians. His imagination worked—and how.

"When the outer rim of the sun sinks behind the horizon, its light breaks apart into the spectrum just as a rainbow does—with the red light at the bottom and the blue at the top. As the sun descends further so does the red color, and the blue disperses into the atmosphere. And at that moment, the last fraction of the visible light may flash in the green color."

"How do you—?" Ethan tried to understand what he just heard. "How do you know all that?"

"Mr. Harper explained it. I was with my dad at his ranch on Saturday. His mare was giving birth, so they called my dad to help and I went with him. We saw it happening from there. Mr. Harper read a lot about space and all that. He knows almost everything about the stars there is to know. He even drew for me on a sheet of paper how the green flash happened."

"Did he?"

"Yes. That's a rare phenomenon, Et. The sky has to be very clear to make it possible for the green flash to happen."

"Wait a minute. Hold it. You said the green flash? Why is it called green when the blue one disperses into the atmosphere, if I got it straight?"

"You got it straight. That's because green is the other primary color of the light."

"Huh?"

"Don't worry. There is the blue flash as well. It's even more beautiful than the green one. But the odds are against the chance of you ever seeing it."

"Why?"

"Because the atmosphere must be very, very, very clear and enough blue light has to penetrate the sky to cause the blue flash to appear. Got it?"

"Huh? A-ha." But Ethan had no idea what Sarah was talking about.

"Cool, right?"

"Yeah. Very cool."

"Okey-dokey. I'm glad you saw it too. I knew you would love it. Well, here's where I'm leaving you. See you later, alligator?"

"In a while, crocodile."

"Oh yes, don't worry. I'll let you know when I find out if aliens visited us."

She waved a fond goodbye and left, hopping in her casual, careless way.

Don't tell anybody, not for the life of you, he wanted to shout after her, but gave up out of fear somebody might hear him.

There was nothing left for him, but to trust Sarah and hope she wouldn't blab what they had talked about. He wouldn't, that's for sure. For the lightning—caused by green and blue colors—kept flashing and flashing in his head. As the years passed, it became clear that Ethan's fears proved unfounded: Sarah knew how to keep secrets and not rat on her friends.

7

In mid-October, the first snowflakes arrived in Greenfield. Early this year, dragging along the New Year as well. But little would change in a small town lulled into its daily and steady routine. Greenfield always had its own rhythm and didn't much care about the changes in other parts of the states. A world onto itself, it remained that way, an oasis of peace in the boiling world.

The struggle of the African-Americans for their civil rights marked the last decade and shook the whole of America. The ominous air of the Vietnam War had crept—and was still creeping—into the pores of every American, and the space race with the Soviet Union was not only a matter of prestige and the spheres of influence, but also of national pride.

That didn't mean the landing of the first Americans on the Moon—Armstrong and Aldrin (representing all the human race)—wasn't greeted with celebration and great joy in Greenfield. Far from it. No one could deny that the news from Memphis of the assassination of Martin Luther King—Baptist preacher and leader of the blacks' Civil Rights Movement was met with shock, disbelief and sorrow. As were the assassinations of John Fitzgerald Kennedy in Dallas and his brother, Robert

Kennedy, five and a half years later.

Although this toll that made history didn't circumvent Greenfield, it seemed as if it had been written there at a slower pace. Or at the very least left traces less deep and wounds less painful that healed more easily. The positive attitudes toward life and high spirits full of optimism contributed a lot to that. Besides, the inhabitants of Greenfield were more focused on themselves and their small town than what happened outside its limits.

That doesn't mean the roiling sixties escaped Greenfield completely. Some Greenfielders lived through it, either vicariously through their relatives and friends scattered all over the United States or personally. To some, the American dream turned into a Vietnam nightmare overnight. They found themselves snatched away from their cozy, little paradise and thrown into the hell of Vietnam's paradise turned war zone.

Not even renowned public figures Joan Baez, Bob Dylan, The Doors and many others together with an even bigger and more euphoric hippie movement could prevent the mass madness and Vietnam hysteria from drawing them into the world of chaos, hatred, murder and terrorism. Those that remained at home in Greenfield sympathized with them and their families, praying for their lives, the end of the war and for their quick return. Not all the prayers had been answered.

Some came back even before the war ended.

In sealed, tin coffins,

or as invalids for life.

Some never returned.

While their families mourned their beloved ones—their children—in peace, silence and dignity, the Flower Power cry for peace and love resounded ever stronger and louder throughout the whole nation. It echoed through the streets of New York City, Washington DC, Boston, San Francisco, Houston, and other American cities demanding the armistice and the end of war.

They wanted the light to return into the hearts of all

Americans.

William Patrick and Ethan McCoy, Jason Hawk and Derrick Zachariah were too young to comprehend the tempest of the time their country was going through.

The democracy of the United States of America was under a serious test.

They knew something big, of historic relevance was going on. But what they occupied themselves with were their school exams and the successes and failures connected to them, their growing up, maturing and their friendship. There was no place for prejudice shaking the entire world in their hearts. They lived for themselves, for Greenfield, with the love they were taught about their whole young lives.

That winter of 1971, when January drew to an end and Greenfield already sank into a deep sleep under the cover of fresh snow, an incident happened that left a deep mark on the rest of Ethan's childhood.

On Saturday afternoon Ethan and Will went sledding. The scant falling snow seemed as if it might stop soon. A chilly north wind blew, freezing breaths into ice, pinching ears, nose and cheeks, and biting the fingers. Most inhabitants of Greenfield, both old and young, were at home sitting in front of fireplaces or stoves.

Buttoned up to their chins and wearing so many layers of clothes they were the size of polar bears, Ethan and Will walked alone in the almost deserted streets—barring several cars buried beneath the snow. Greenfield had turned into a ghost town within several hours. One of snow, wind, and silence.

Will's boots squeaked in the fluttery snow as he pulled the sled along. Ethan followed him, walking on the trodden trail. When they reached the elevation, Ethan took over the sled to give his brother a break. Then they ascended the hill.

Reaching the top, they sat on the sled one behind the other

and went downhill.

The first ride was nothing special because of the large amount of snow. First, they had to make a compacted path. Ethan and Will didn't want to give up.

Ten attempts later they glided along smoothly. Their efforts having been worth the trouble.

The snow had a perfect consistency, they couldn't resist building a snowman. As they rolled the big head onto the huge body, it became clear they didn't have all the requisites to finish it. They agreed to make an even larger snowman in their back-yard. One with a pan, the carrot, the broom and the scarf. Nor would they forget the mouth or the eyes. The only question that came to mind was what to do with the half-finished one. Ethan, quick to solve the problem, pushed his brother into the snow-man. Will took two seconds to clamber out of the snowman's hug—which gave Ethan time to speed downhill, fleeing from him.

As soon as he got his boots back on the frozen ground, Will dashed after him. No matter how fast he was, Ethan was always a fraction faster. He flew on the wings of fear.

Seeing that Ethan had no intention of stopping, he called his name and ran even faster.

"Ethan!" he called after him, as he ran, trying to catch his brother's attention. He tried to warn him of the approaching danger. That danger didn't come from a vengeful Will, but from the river Ethan closed in on with every step.

Will broke out in a cold sweat. He realized he had no chance to catch up with his brother, plus his strength also failed him. He saw the river lurking in the silence. The night falling. And he envisioned his brother running out onto the ice, and the ice breaking under him, pulling him down into the cold embrace of the main stream of the river.

"Ethan, stop!" he cried out.

Ethan stopped at last. He stood several steps from the river, gazing at the snow in front of him. He turned around as he heard the squeaking of the snow getting closer.

"Willy—" he uttered.

"You idiot!" Will leapt on him, pulling him into the snow and covering him with his body. "Are you crazy?!" he stormed. "You could have ended up in the river. You could have gotten yourself killed."

"Willy," he tried to free himself. "Get off, get away from me."

"Not only will I not get away from you, but I'll beat the hell out of you. What were you thinking, you fool? To commit suicide?"

"Will, you're crushing me. Please—"

"I could make you eat this snow!" He rubbed a handful of snow onto Ethan's face and pushed himself up. He reached out his hand. "Get up. We will collect the sled and then we are going home. Winter joys are over for today."

"You go," Ethan said, breathing heavily. "I'll wait here."

Will eyed him from head to foot, a suspicious look in his eyes.

"Do you think I would leave you alone here? Just a few steps from the half-frozen river? If you think so, you're as crazy as a loon."

"Please, Will. I'm tired from running. I have no strength left. I will wait for you here. Won't do anything stupid, I give you my word."

"I wonder which one of us is more nuts," Will gave up. "Wait for me here, then. Be sure not to move a single inch from where you're standing, or you are in a big trouble."

"Don't worry. I'll be fine," Ethan jumped about the place rubbing his palms against each other. "And hurry, before it gets full dark."

"I'll be back in a few minutes. And be careful. I'm warning you."

He turned around several times to check whether Ethan was in the same place as when he left him and then sped up.

This time he raced against the darkness, which was in a hurry to envelop everything.

He wondered who would win that race.

Will followed the trodden footprints. He was glad he took his father's advice and brought along a flashlight. The night fell upon them sooner than expected and the flashlight would come in handy.

He hurried as fast as he could, lest Ethan froze from waiting too long. Getting colder by the second, Will was hot and wet from his own perspiration beneath the thick jacket, woolen pull-over and a thermos-shirt. He hoped Ethan was all right and that he wouldn't catch a cold. How would he explain that to his mother?

He didn't know how to explain to himself Ethan's flight into certain death. How could Ethan not be aware of the danger? His brother wasn't stupid. What came over him? He kept asking himself. Perhaps Will shouldn't have left him alone?

Relieved to see the figure of his brother lit by the flashlight, he left the sled and ran the few remaining steps. Something seemed off to him.

Ethan crouched in the snow, his arms tight around his shoulders. His chin lay against his breast. And he only had on the turtleneck sweater and a vest.

Stunned by doubts mixed with fear Will suppressed a cry.

"Et, where is your jacket?"

Ethan raised his head and put up a pale smile.

"Et! What's the matter with you? What happened? Tell me what you did with your jacket."

"There. . . ." he motioned toward the river in a slow move-ment of his frozen arm.

"Where, there?"

"It's on the riverbank." He rose and tottered at the first step.

Will took his jacket off and wrapped it around his brother. Then he grabbed the sled and, pushing his brother along, hissed: "We'll get it. I hope you have a good explanation for this."

"Yes, my dear brother, I do. A very good explanation."

Will looked at him as if he was hallucinating but said nothing. He followed him, lighting up the way.

"Wait! Where are you going?" He stopped when they reached the river.

The crusted January River was covered with a thin layer of ice on which the fresh snow had fallen.

"We can't go any farther."

"We got to go on a bit more, down the stream. We must follow the footprints. My jacket is down there."

"Et, can you explain what's going on? I asked you not to go anywhere, and now you are taking me for a walk along the bank of a frozen river in the night? Do you want us to break the ice and both sink into the water?"

"Don't worry, we won't. I've already walked this way. And we would have been there already, hadn't you asked all those questions."

Life returned into Ethan. His blood circulated again in his numb extremities. As if he were waking up from a deep sleep.

Twenty yards down the stream Ethan stopped himself. He took the flashlight from Will's hand and lit up the snow. When he found what he was looking for, he returned the flashlight to Will and walked toward his jacket.

He kneeled in the snow and uncovered it.

Will came nearer. His face pulled into a grimace.

"What? It's a—"

"It's a dog, Willy! I think he's still alive. I don't know how much longer he can last, so we better hurry. Help me put him on the sled!"

Will stood as if paralyzed. Everything spun inside his head.

"But how? Where from? Are you sure—"

"Will, wake up!" Ethan's suppressed excitement erupted. "We must help him. We can't just leave him here like that. He'll freeze to death. Look at him, how poor and helpless he is. He can barely breathe. I gave him a massage while you were away, but I don't know whether it did any good. We must move right away, Will. We must move now."

Will kept the flashlight directed at the body covered in wet, frozen hair.

"I think he's dead, Et."

"He will be if you don't move your ass." Ethan surprised himself at his own temper when he snapped at his brother. But it worked. Will moved.

"Whose dog is it? And how did it get here?"

"Are there any grasshoppers on the Orion?"

"What?"

"I said I didn't know. It doesn't matter now. What matters is that we're here, and that he needs our help."

"You keep him and don't let him fall off. I'll pull the sled," Will said, after putting the dog on the sled as snug as it was possible.

They walked in silence, sinking into their thoughts and the snow.

"How did you find him?" Will asked again, when they reached the light of the street lamps. He turned around to take a better look at the dog, but the sight of the numb body under the jacket just cramped his heart.

"By the nose. I sniffed him up."

"What's the matter with you? Why are you so curt? I asked you politely, and I deserve a polite answer."

"Sorry. It drives me crazy how slowly we're going. I'm afraid he won't make it. That everything's in vain."

"Don't worry, he'll make it," Will consoled him. "If he has made it up till now, he will manage a little more."

"I saw the footprints in the snow. They were bloody. I felt somebody was in trouble, so I had to check it out. I found him on the riverbank covered in snow."

"But why didn't you wait for me? We could have gone together."

"You want the truth? I was afraid you wouldn't want to go because it was getting dark already. That's why I sent you alone to bring the sled. I wanted to take a closer look at whose footprints those were, but I figured you wouldn't want to do that. And that you wouldn't let me, either."

"You figured it out correctly."

"That also means I did the right thing by sending you alone to bring up the sled."

"That's something we still must find out." Will was serious.

"Willy?"

"What?"

"Are you mad at me?"

"No."

"Sure?"

"I'm not mad at you." He tried to push away the thought about what could have happened had his brother found a wounded or starving coyote. No point in thinking about that right now. Let bygones be bygones.

"What shall we do with the dog?"

Will stopped short. He turned around and faced his brother, intending to snap at him, but changed his mind and continued to pull the sled again.

"I thought we could keep him. If Father agrees."

"Et, who knows whose dog this is? Who knows whether he'll survive? Who knows whether he's still alive! What he needs now is medical treatment if he can be helped at all. Therefore, forget about any plans about the future. We'll think about that when the time comes. What I do know is that we have to ask around and see who he belongs to."

"Will, he will survive, right? He must survive."

"May God help him. We are trying our best."

Heavy snow fell again when they reached home.

"Et, you better go in and tell Mum and Dad about what happened. Call Ben Zachariah and tell him I'm on my way with a dying dog so he can prepare everything. And you better change right away if you don't want to catch a cold: that's the only thing we're still missing."

"But I want to go with you. I won't leave you alone. . . ."

"Et, listen to what I say. Somebody *has* to tell Father. The dog can't wait much longer. The better prepared Ben Zachariah is by the time I get there, the greater the dog's chances of survival."

"Why don't you stay home? I'll take him—"

"You're staying here, period," Will brushed him off. "You're wet and frozen, and you are slower because you're smaller and weaker. Besides, you're stealing my time."

He turned around and without another word went down the street, pulling the sled with the wounded dog.

Ethan ran into the house.

As he approached the Zachariah home, Will spotted the big figure of the vet, Benjamin Zachariah, coming out of the house, stumbling and skidding on the snow as he tried to rush toward him.

"Good evening, Mr. Zachariah."

"Hello, Will. I can't say the evening is good, judging by the weather. Your father has called. I understand you've had an adventure?"

"Yes. Ethan and I went sledding. Upon returning, we found this dog. Et found him."

"You're brave boys for going out in this weather."

"Oh, it's nothing." But the praise made Will feel good.

Benjamin Zachariah burst into the house carrying the dog in his arms while Will leaned the sled against the wall next to the entrance door.

"Wait for me in the guest room. And make yourself comfortable. Take off your boots and wet clothes. My wife will be down in a minute with the hot chocolate and something for you to put on."

"Why, thank you, you don't have to. . . ."

Ethan stood at the window of his room, watching the snow fall. He was bathed, dried and warmed up. Two hours had passed since he and Will parted, and his brother still hadn't come back.

Nor had he called either.

What was going on? What happened to Willy? What happened to the dog? Ethan bit his fingernails.

His mother came twice to ask if he needed anything, but he just shook his head. What he needed was information. The knowledge of whether the dog was alive or dead, whatever was the case. The uncertainty drove him crazy.

That Will hadn't come back yet might be a good sign. It should mean the dog was alive and Ben Zachariah was operating. But what if he brought him around and he died then? Or remained in a coma? What would he do with such a dog? He would have to put him to sleep. Why bother with all this in the first place in that case?

A knock sounded at the door. Ira McCoy again.

"Thanks, Mother, for worrying, but I don't need anything."

"Ethan, Will has arrived."

"Will! What did he, is—?"

"Come on down. He's waiting for you."

Ethan couldn't remember when he dashed down the stairs at a greater speed. He exploded into the living room where his father, brother, and Ben Zachariah waited.

"Boy, is that the way to get down the stairs?" his father reprimanded him.

"I apologize. I didn't mean. . . ."

"Well, Sean, I better go," Ben Zachariah said. "The mere thought of going out into that freeze gives me the creeps. Can't wait to get home. Good night, Ira. Night, boys. Sean," he nodded a farewell and headed for the door.

"Good night, Ben," Ira McCoy responded.

"'Night, Mr. Zachariah. Thanks a lot for the clothes," Will said.

"Not at all. You can bring them back when the blizzard stops."

"Sure. Say hello to Der and Sarah once again for me."

Ethan stood helpless and as dumbstruck, waiting for the verdict.

"Sit down, son." His father came to him and put his hand on Ethan's shoulder.

"Thank you, but I think I'll keep standing. What happened to the dog?" He couldn't wait any more. "Is he dead?"

"The dog's alive, Ethan, though his condition's very serious."

He's alive! The dog is alive. Ethan didn't hear the other part of the sentence.

"A big question is whether he'll live through the night," Sean McCoy said, carefully, seeing hope on Ethan's face.

"He's alive." Ethan's eyes filled up with tears of joy.

"Ethan, did you hear me?"

"He's alive, Father. He's alive!"

"The dog was almost frozen to death. He has heavy frost bite. And he's starved and exhausted."

Ethan looked at his father not understanding.

"He had wounds on his paws and body. Ben treated them as best as he could. It's a miracle he stayed alive."

"But he has! He's *alive!*"

"Et, do you understand what Dad's saying?" Will looked at his brother.

"Yes, Will. The dog's alive. You and I, we saved him. That's what Dad's talking about."

"No, Et. Dad's trying to tell you that the dog is—"

"That's right, son. You saved him," Sean McCoy interrupted Will, giving him a sign to let him take over. "For the time being. But he has a long and heavy battle before him. You have done everything you could. I repeat, Ethan, you did what you could. The rest is up to him. He must gather strength and fight. It's his fight, not yours."

"He will. I know he will make it. He'll pull himself through. He's a tough dog. He proved that already."

William Patrick and Sean McCoy exchanged glances. Ira McCoy watched them from aside, not interfering.

"He's a real fighter." Ethan's faith didn't abandon him.

"Let's hope so." Sean McCoy wished the dog had as much

strength as his son had faith. He turned to Will. "I suggest you change and wash and then let's have supper. I think we could all do with something in our stomachs, something to warm us up and refresh us a little."

"All right, sir."

"Will?" Ethan followed him upstairs.

"Yes?"

"Did Ben Zachariah say what sort of dog he was?"

"You mean what breed?"

Ethan nodded in the acknowledgment.

"Yes. He's a golden retriever, Et. A golden retriever."

"A golden retriever," Ethan repeated it as if in a dream.

A golden retriever.

8

The telephone rang very early at the Zachariah home, the next morning. Ethan. Benjamin Zachariah picked up the phone. "Morning, Ethan. How are you?"

"Thanks for asking, Mr. Zachariah, I'm fine."

"How can I help you? Or was it Derrick or Sarah that you called for?"

"Actually, it's you I need. I wished to thank you for everything you've done. I didn't get that yesterday. Thank you very much for helping us out."

"That's all right, Ethan, it's my job. But it's nice of you to have called. Besides, I must tell you, you and your brother have done a big, noble thing yesterday. Maybe you have even saved a life."

Ethan blushed on the other side of the phone.

"Well, thank you. I wanted to ask you about the dog's condition. Is he okay?"

"Ethan, there's something I want you to understand. This is a nice, big and strong dog."

"I know. Will said it's a golden retriever."

"That's right. But you must be aware of his condition when you found him. It would be dangerous even for much tougher dogs, with much greater stamina. I have no intention of discouraging you or making you sad. I want to be frank with you—his condition is still critical."

"How critical?"

"Very critical. I can't say anything for sure yet. He may get away with it, or he may succumb. His chances are about even."

"Those chances are not too promising," Ethan said with a sad voice.

"I'm sorry, Ethan. I want you to know I'm doing my best. You shouldn't worry about that. He's in good hands."

"I've never doubted you for a minute, Mr. Zachariah. If anybody in this world can help him it's you. And I'm sure you will."

"Thank you, Ethan. I have a suggestion for you. Although I don't think it's a good idea, would you like to come and see him for a moment?"

"May I? May I, Mr. Zachariah?" Ethan's voice raised a decibel or two. "That's what I wanted to ask you, but I didn't have the courage. I thought you'd turn me down."

"I wouldn't have turned you down. I must warn you, though, the dog doesn't look well at all. He looks hardly any better than yesterday. He's fighting for his life, Ethan. I have second thoughts, it might be better you don't see him yet. I'm afraid it'll be hard for you."

"Don't worry, I'll be okay. I want to see him. Just for a moment."

"Very well then. Come in the afternoon after lunch. You can be with him a short time—as we have agreed. Some improvements might turn up by then."

"Thank you very much. I wonder if there's anything else I can do?"

"You've done enough already. Be patient and have faith. Believe he will pull through."

Ben Zachariah put down the receiver and smiled at his daughter who observed him from the door.

"Who was it, Daddy?"

"Ethan McCoy, sweetie."

"He called about the dog?"

"Yes. He made inquiries about his condition. Ethan's coming to see him this afternoon."

He embraced the girl around her shoulders, and she put her arm around his waist.

"You know, I have a feeling Ethan will hang around in our house for the next couple of days," he added.

Sarah's eyes remained enigmatic, hiding any emotion her father's words might have triggered.

Ethan remembered those moments, even after twenty-four years, as if they happened only yesterday. He felt awkward for having burst out crying in the ambulance at the first meeting with the golden retriever. It was more than he could bear. Benjamin Zachariah appreciated the situation, and Ethan could swear he saw tears in his eyes, too. It was normal to feel that way. Benjamin shared the same feelings as Ethan for the dog fighting for every hour of his life. Ethan knew something precious between him and the good-hearted veterinarian was born then. Something that would make them close and bond them together in the years to come, when life would take a rather different course.

In the next several days Ethan spent all his free time beside the sick dog. Even his parents didn't bother him with the usual household chores as they used to. It seemed as if it was their contribution to the slow, unpromising recovery of the helpless dog. Ethan couldn't describe the gratitude he felt toward them for their generosity. How much more grateful he would have been had he known his father talked to Ben Zachariah, saying not to spare either the means or the effort to save the dog. He promised to pay all the expenses. The secret agreement would remain between the two longtime friends. His father didn't want Ethan to know about that. To Sean McCoy money didn't mean much, anyway. The only thing that interested him was his son and his well-being. He understood Ethan's attachment to the dog, and he also knew how Ethan would feel if he lost him. Sean McCoy couldn't afford that to happen. He couldn't allow his son to suffer, so he talked Ben Zachariah into letting him pay for the recovery of the dog. Reluctantly, Ben Zachariah accepted.

While Ethan sat beside the dog looking at him—doing nothing and saying nothing—Sarah, Derrick, Jason and Will took turns keeping him company. They thought their presence might speed up the dog's recovery and reduce the number of days Ethan had to worry. They showed their true friendship in time of distress. Although they didn't speak much or ask many questions—outside of a few words of encouragement, consolation or hope—it meant a lot to Ethan. The only thing he didn't know was how the dog took the stroking and whispering words of sympathy and support. He remained motionless, showing no reaction. What Ethan was interested in the most: How did the dog feel? Was he any better? Would he pull through? If so, when?

Ethan had no doubt the dog would heal, but when? The big question, and nobody could tell him the answer.

Sarah was with Ethan. They talked quietly. Already for the umpteenth time they recollected how Ethan and Will had found the dog and what happened from that night to the present day. And they never tired of talking about an unusual event in Greenfield that changed its rhythm of life, if only for a short time. Sarah and Ethan, unaccustomed to life in Greenfield shrouded in a veil of secrecy, considered the appearance of a dog amid a snowy blizzard a first-rate sensation. Their blood circulated faster, and their eyes shone whenever they thought of the event and the mysterious dog. The dog that still didn't look like a dog. He resembled a plush toy similar to the one Ethan used to play with as a child. He stroked its head tenderly. Then the toy came to life.

Ethan withdrew his hand and cried out. He startled Sarah with his cry, making her jump from her chair. She covered her mouth with a hand to suppress her cry.

Ethan's heart beat wildly as he moved his hand in slow motion toward the dog's nose. He halted in front of the dog's nostrils and tried to steady his trembling hand.

Several seconds passed, and the dog licked his hand again.

A moment later he opened his eyes.

Ethan stared at Sarah, his eyes wide as she clenched her fingers into fists and shot them in the air celebrating victory and success. A big smile spread across her face, like the one on Ethan's.

He also raised his fist and waved it through the air. Sarah then clapped her hands in appreciation.

Ethan turned back to the dog and looked into his brown eyes. They were clean and clear.

Ethan leaned and pressed his head against the dog's. He felt his warm breath on his face and rough tongue licking his neck.

The happiest moment of his life.

About three weeks later, the dog had fully recovered. Thanks to Benjamin Zachariah's golden hands, his past beauty returned too. With healing, the time came to look for his guardian. Ethan's heart was heavy at the thought of having to part with his new friend, but he caused no trouble to Benjamin when he advertised finding the dog.

"I know it's not easy for you, Ethan, but we have to do it. That's the right thing to do. Imagine how you'd feel if you learned somebody found the dog you'd lost hope of ever seeing again. Try to imagine their feelings right now. And what the dog must feel too. He longs for them. No matter how much you like him and he likes you, we must keep in mind that there is someone else who likes him even more."

"And what if there's no such person?" Ethan refused to let go of hope. "Or, he may have been abandoned until somebody found him?"

"In that case the fairest solution would be the dog goes to the one who found him. Under the condition that the one who found him wants him."

"Oh, this one wants him." Ethan pointed at himself with his thumb. "He wants him badly."

Three days passed with nobody replying to the ad. Ethan hoped it would remain that way. He also sent several prayers to the Almighty, just in case and to be on the safe side.

Tuesday passed, followed by Wednesday, and Ethan approached the weekend with optimism. If nobody claimed him by then, the dog would be his.

This case proved that hope is the last to die. Ethan's hope almost died when Benjamin Zachariah called on Thursday before noon. Warren Preston—the boy Sarah hit in the head with a chair—visited him, inquiring about the dog. He claimed the dog was his, but the dog's reaction wasn't that of a happy dog being reunited with his before-lost-and-now-found guardian. When the dog snarled, Warren announced his father would drop by tomorrow to confirm the dog belonged to him. Ben thought Ethan—his savior and a temporary guardian—would like to be with the dog when they arrived. Ethan thanked him and said he would be there for sure. He also asked whether he could bring his brother with him. Ben saw no reason why not since they both found the dog.

That night didn't bring much sleep to Ethan. He barely closed his eyes until the morning dawned. He spent the whole night praying, musing and thinking about the dog, looking at the moon through the window and, most of all, tossing around in his bed.

In the morning Ethan looked drowsy, pale, with bloodshot eyes and fat, black rings underlining them. The price to pay for a sleepless night. Every few minutes Ben Zachariah threw worried glances at him. He looked at Will with a question in his eyes, but Will merely shrugged. "He didn't sleep a wink last night."

"Looks like the past night was a hard one for all of us," was all Benjamin could say. There was no time for anything else. The voices of Warren and Bill Preston could be heard down the hall as his wife let them in.

"Be brave, boys. Everything will be fine," he said,

encouraging Will and Ethan before he left to welcome the guests.

Ethan suppressed a sob in his throat.

The dog sat at peace beside Ethan's left leg and Will stood at his brother's right side when Ben with the father and the son Preston entered.

"Boys, you know Mr. Preston and his son Warren," Ben Zachariah said, trying to break the tense atmosphere.

Ethan and Will nodded a silent greeting.

"They've come about my ad to find out whether the dog you found is theirs. I hope you don't mind them seeing him."

"No," they answered, though Ethan wished they disappeared the moment they stepped into the room. He wished they would disappear into thin air or become just part of a bad dream.

Judging from how the dog stiffened when the newcomers came in, he shared the same opinion.

"Go ahead, Warren," Benjamin Zachariah encouraged him. "Check up and see whether this is Max."

Warren gave him a sour look and moved a few short steps toward Ethan, Will and the dog.

His mouth closed, the dog growled.

Warren took two more steps, and the growling turned into snarling.

Warren stopped, not knowing what to do and looked at his father. Bill Preston nodded to him to go on and Warren moved closer to the dog.

The dog stiffened and, bracing himself for an attack, barked.

Ethan stretched his hand toward the dog, but Will put his hand on his shoulder, warning him not to meddle. The dog and the Prestons had to find their own way out of this situation.

Warren Preston found the way out by retreating. In a pleading voice, he turned to his father: "He will bite me if I move a step forward. Dad, would you try it?"

"Warren, are you sure this is Max?" Benjamin Zachariah took advantage of the moment of confusion. "He's not behaving as if you two know each other."

"I'm positive. I don't know what's come over him. He acted like that yesterday too."

"Had you gone through the same thing he has, you wouldn't behave any different, either," Ethan said, unable to resist.

Warren ignored Ethan. "Dad, I beg you. You try."

Bill Preston watched the dog snuggle up against Ethan's leg and stop barking the moment Warren withdrew. With tender and comforting strokes Ethan caressed the dog's head. Bill Preston observed that the boy's touch had a soothing effect on the dog.

He cleared his throat and said, "Warren, I'm sorry. But I'm not sure this is Max. Max didn't behave like that. Max was peaceful. Max was a nice dog. But this. . . . I think we came here for nothing."

"Dad? How could you say that? This is Max. I know it. You heard Ethan. He admitted the dog couldn't look better after all he has been through. And Max strayed less than a month ago." He sent a waspish smile to Ethan, taking advantage of his rash remark.

Ethan would burn him to ashes with his look if he only could.

"You cannot prove that, son." Unlike Warren, Bill Preston tried to be reasonable.

"But I can. I can prove that."

They all waited in expectation, and Ethan stopped breathing.

"He has a scar behind his right ear, which runs to the half of his neck. That's where Killer got him by accident half a year ago. If that dog has such a scar, then he's Max."

Ethan choked. He looked at Ben Zachariah, who returned his glance. He saw support in his eyes, but also the first signs of insecurity.

Warren was merciless to the end.

"All we have to do is to find out if this dog has such a scar and the problem's solved." He rejoiced in triumph, grinning with malice at Ethan and Will. Carried away by his emotions and sniffing a victory, he made but one fatal mistake. "Well, Dad, look at him. You're not afraid of Max, are you?"

Bill Preston turned pale and then he blushed. He whipped his son with a scornful look.

Warren realized the mistake he made and became livid. He wished the earth swallowed him. Together with the damned McCoys and the stupid dog.

Ethan, Will and Ben Zachariah exchanged glances, waiting to see what would happen next.

What happened next was that Bill Preston moved toward the dog.

Ethan's heart pumped so wildly he thought it would burst in his chest and made him drop on the floor.

Bill Preston approached the dog talking softly to him, and the dog wagged his tail. He kneeled before him, stroked his head and run his fingers through his long hair, and the dog pushed his body against his leg in affection as if they were old acquaintances and friends.

Ethan's eyes gleamed with tears, Warren's with triumph.

Before Ethan burst out crying, Bill Preston stood up, gave the dog one final pat on the head and asked Ben Zachariah to join him outside the room.

The three boys looked at each other in disbelief. There was embarrassment in Will's eyes, uncertainty in Ethan's, and shock in Warren's.

Warren shot a piercing look at the dog and Ethan, but said nothing. Neither did Will, who had been quiet the entire time. They waited in silence for the two men to return.

Ethan searched for the answer in Ben Zachariah's face, but it was expressionless.

Bill Preston gave the answer they waited for.

"I thank you, boys, for being so kind and doing us a favor. I apologize for any inconvenience we may have caused you. Have a nice day."

He approached his son who gaped at him with his mouth wide open and grabbed him under his arm.

"Let's go, Warren. Mother's waiting for us. We've stayed too long here."

Will wanted to yell with joy when the door closed behind them, but stopped short upon seeing consternation and the lack of understanding on his brother's face. He looked at Ethan with a question in his eyes. Ethan looked at Ben Zachariah, waiting for an explanation. Only Ben Zachariah acted normally. He was calm, relaxed, and his face carried an expression of justice being served.

"But," Ethan said, looking confused, "I don't understand anything."

"The dog's yours, Et! How come you don't understand it?" Will grabbed him by the shoulders and shook him. "This isn't Max." He couldn't control his excitement anymore.

"But that's the thing. This *is* Max!"

Will stood as if petrified. He gaped at his brother as if he had gone mad.

"What did you say? Say it again?"

"This is Max, Willy. I don't know how Mr. Preston didn't see that?"

"You're nuts! You're completely nuts!"

"No, I'm not. He has the exact scar as Warren described." He leaned down toward the dog, moved his hair away and showed the scar to his brother.

Will's mouth opened in disbelief.

"But besides that scar, Max has a few others," Benjamin Zachariah's voice came from a distance. Sounding like that of a ghost, it grabbed the attention of the confused boys. "Just like the one on his neck, Bill Preston saw them too."

To spare himself additional questions, he continued, "That is Max indeed. Bill Preston told me in the hall. That's why he asked me to go aside with him. To do him a favor. He asked me whether I could keep the dog or find someone who will take him."

Ethan gulped.

Benjamin Zachariah carried on: "Max was very unhappy

with them. The Prestons took him from Hodders when they got the baby girl. Max couldn't stay with them any longer—though he'd become the favorite of everyone—because little Tena was allergic to the dog hair. They wanted all the best for Max as they gave him away to Bill Preston in faith he would get accustomed to them. Prestons already had one dog—Killer, the Doberman. Warren gave him that name for fun, but it turned out to be becoming to him. Not to say, well deserved.

"Max was only several months old when he came to the Prestons, but Killer never accepted him. Not even as a puppy. He always watched for a chance to attack him. He was jealous. And he became revengeful, malicious. Killer and Max came to blows several times. Warren never admitted that to his father, but Bill saw it from the wounds both dogs had. After each fight Max disappeared for a while and returned only when the hunger compelled him to. As their fighting continued, Max would be missing for longer periods of time. Until he disappeared, and you found him.

"That's not the whole story. Bill had doubts about something he couldn't prove. He suspected Warren forced the dogs to fight and dislike each other. He suspected he organized dog-fights between his two dogs, which always took place when Bill was absent from home. His wife was too busy with their two-year-old daughter Janet and couldn't check on Warren and his friends playing in the barn. That the barn was away from the house came in handy for them to practice their low instincts.

"Today, Bill Preston got the proof he was looking for. Max gave it to him when he snarled at Warren, threatening to bite him should he come closer. And when Max allowed Bill Preston to stroke him, everything became obvious. He made up his mind and asked for my opinion. I advised him not to say anything to Warren and leave Max with the two of you. Bill saw how close you and Max have become and how well you got along. That's why he agreed without much thinking. Thus, Max remains here, and he's yours, if you still want him."

The rejoicing roared through Ben Zachariah's clinic and

home. Max joined the overjoyed boys, jumping and barking.

Will hugged his brother. "We made it, Et. We did it. Max's yours. He stays with us."

Ben Zachariah put his hands on their shoulders and said, "Let me know, boys, when you are ready to take him home. I still have to give him vitamin shots and instruct you how to feed him at the beginning."

"Now. He goes with us right away." Ethan didn't hesitate for a moment.

Ben Zachariah laughed. "I figured you'd say that. If you give me a few minutes, I'll go prepare Max and then the three of you can go home together."

Minutes later they stepped out of the vet's home into the bright sunlight. The snow under their feet had softened, melting in the warmth. Ethan and Will walked with long, satisfied and confident strides, while Max hopped around them in the wet snow. As if reborn and joyful with the advancing spring, the dog headed toward his new home.

"Imagine Mom and Dad's surprised faces when they see us with Max. I hope we don't startle Dad too much. He's had enough troubles with his heart this winter."

"Don't worry. I'm sure they'll be surprised, but pleasantly. I know Father. Especially when he sees what a handsome dog River is. River will win him over at first glance, you wait and see."

"River?"

"Yes, Willy. Have you forgotten? This isn't Max. How would Warren react if he heard we named a stray dog after his noble and most beloved Max? He'd never forgive us. Fortunately, this is River, not Warren's lost Max."

"But, why River, Et? Why River? It makes no sense. Everybody will laugh at us."

"On the contrary. It makes a lot of sense. Didn't we find him along the river? There's no name more suitable for our dog than—January River."

Will looked at his brother.

"*January River?* Bro, I'm not William Patrick McCoy if you didn't know from the beginning you'd give him this name. Even before you knew he was yours."

"Right from the start. From the moment I spotted him."

"And then, once he healed, you knew he'd be yours."

"You've figured it right."

"I wouldn't be surprised if you told me you brought him back from the dead, or somehow influenced the course of events."

"Maybe I did."

"So, you are a shaman or something?"

"Now, you're getting to know your younger brother," Ethan said, with just a hint of a smile.

9

In the next eighteen months, Ethan, Derrick, Jason and Sarah all reached the age of fourteen and Will was almost seventeen. It was a time filled with unlimited happiness for this close bunch of Greenfield friends. River, or Riv as Ethan fondly called him, contributed much to this and soon became their honorary member. He had also found a prominent place in Ethan's bed, thus provoking many arguments with Ethan's disapproving parents. Each time, when the storm subsided in McCoys' home, River crawled back into his favorite spot and the two of them fell into undisturbed sleep together. Ethan and River became inseparable, almost literally.

Not everybody in Greenfield looked with benevolence at Ethan and his dog. Ethan avoided Warren Preston whenever he could. He remembered the chilling look Warren gave him when they first met after the scene in Ben Zachariah's ambulance. He also remembered the threat and desire for revenge radiating from Warren's cold eyes. Ethan McCoy was smart enough to stay away from them. There were moments when he had to meet them, when retreating was impossible. On such occasions, Ethan winced from the look that didn't leave him indifferent even today.

Even after all these months Warren's look didn't calm down. Nor did it stop Ethan from worrying. He knew something was about to happen, something bad and frightening. The only way he could prevent it was by staying alert and ready all the time. The thought of what might happen terrified Ethan so much it made him nervous. Never far from his thoughts, it prevented him from enjoying the full happiness of summer days.

One late summer evening while the McCoy family gathered for supper, the doorbell rang. Will opened the door and Sergeant Byron, sheriff of the police station in Greenfield, entered the house. His arrival had nothing to do with the disappearance of Ethan's dog which he feared all the time (River peacefully lay beside Ethan's chair), but the news he brought was equally, if not even more, shocking.

Derrick Zachariah had disappeared.

Derrick's parents called the sheriff's office and reported the disappearance of their son. Derrick left home early that morning and hadn't come back yet. He never said where he was going, except that he might go rafting with the boys (Jason, Ethan and Will), but it wasn't certain. With the weather unstable that morning, a summer storm seemed imminent for later in the day. But it bypassed Greenfield. After Derrick's worried parents called his friends—who all made it home safely—and learned nothing about their son's whereabouts, they turned to the police and reported him missing. The sheriff, also a friend of the Zachariah's, promised to launch a search in case Derrick did not turn up by morning. He wanted to talk to all of Derrick's friends in the meantime: maybe they could provide useful information. He had already talked to Jason Hawk and now he wanted to ask Ethan and Will a few questions.

Will and Ethan answered with as many details as they could—as Jason had one hour ago—and Sheriff Byron wrote them all down. However, he didn't learn much more than what Deborah and Ben Zachariah had told him already. To Sheriff Woodrow Byron, the most interesting was what he heard from Derrick's younger sister, Sarah. She caught a cold in the middle of summer and had been confined to bed for two days. Sarah noticed Derrick seemed kind of jittery and more excited than usual that morning. Secretive too. He didn't want to tell her anything of his plans when she asked him what he intended to do that day. Though she suspected something wasn't right, she was groggy from the medicine she took and fell asleep. When she woke up, she didn't think about their conversation. Certain that Derrick was having a good time with his friends somewhere, she was sorry she couldn't be with them. Woodrow Byron circled the parts of her statement with a fountain pen. The only starting points in his investigation.

After he had finished with Ethan and Will, he asked them to let him know immediately should they make any contact with Derrick. He then apologized and wished them a good night. Ethan and Will exchanged glances. Both had a premonition that night wouldn't be a good one.

The search party set out at daybreak the next morning. Officially, they considered Derrick Zachariah missing. Only a short time had passed, and the telephone rang in the Zachariah house. The sheriff tried to explain to a hysterical Deborah Zachariah that they had not found Derrick yet. Deborah couldn't be calmed. She kept yelling "Derrick, Derrick," into the receiver until Ben Zachariah took it away from her by force. Then he learned they had found Derrick's belongings on the bridge. Ben promised Sheriff Byron he would be there as quickly as possible. Before he left, he tried to calm down his wife.

"But, Ben, his glasses," Derrick's mother cried. "He never leaves them. He only takes them off when he bathes. He can't see a thing without them. If they found his glasses. . . . Oh, Ben. Oh, Ben. Derrick's *dead*!"

Ben Zachariah gave her a tranquilizer and jumped into his old Buick. With wheels squealing, he sped off toward the bridge.

But he couldn't reach the bridge. Patrol cars blocked both drives leading to the metal construction erected at the spot where the January River was deepest. Benjamin Zachariah had no idea there were so many patrol cars in Greenfield. It felt as if he'd wound up in a gangster movie playing the leading role.

Apart from the police officers' vehicles, an ambulance was present along with a crowd of his fellow townsmen. The news of Derrick's disappearance spread through Greenfield like wildfire. The air buzzed with conversation while everyone waited for further news.

Sergeant Byron approached him and, guiding him between police cars, took him to the place where Derrick's belongings had been found. His T-shirt, short pants, sneakers and glasses were all tucked up neatly. Seeing them, Ben Zachariah realized the gravity of the situation. It took a strong will and a good self-control to hold back the tears. Thank God, Deborah wasn't here, he thought. This would crush her.

He gazed down the river that disappeared into the distance, trying to penetrate its surface right down to the body of his son.

"But why, Derrick? Why?" was all he managed to whisper.

The Scottsbluff diving team, trained for quick and delicate intervention, came in to help. They searched the river under the cover of the night until the gentle dawning light of the next morning, while the policemen with their dogs searched the area and the fields along the riverbanks. Again, nothing.

The fellow Greenfielders flooded the scene in increasing numbers, replacing one another as honorary guard. Rumors circulated, "Won't find him easily. Stream must've taken him down to the North Platte by now. Bet he got entwined in the water shrubs. . . ." But there were also those who had a more positive approach, having faith in the rescue team from Scottsbluff. And others who watched the rescue efforts, keeping their thoughts to themselves.

Ethan, Will and Jason were among the latter. So was River, who couldn't have said anything even if anybody asked his opinion.

They found Derrick's body after two days and one night of

searching. Entwined in the underwater shrubs and roots, about a half a mile upstream from the estuary in the North Platte.

The autopsy report ruled the cause of death as drowning. The wound on Derrick's head remained a riddle. Though not lethal, the coroner believed the victim collided with a construction of the bridge, or—less probable—the bottom of the river. Either one could have caused Derrick to lose consciousness which resulted in his drowning.

The authorities did not suspect murder.

No motive, no signs of violence, and Derrick's neatly tucked belongings pointed to one thing: he dove off the bridge of his own free will.

Derrick's death was premeditated by no one other than himself.

His reason behind it remained a mystery.

Ethan's fears and dark premonitions materialized in the worst possible way and became a reality.

10

Some people are lucky enough and they grow up within the normal and expected time.

For others, their boyhoods are prolonged, because they take their time.

Some never do—they remain children forever.

And then there are those who are forced to grow up before knowing what life really means. Their childhood is over in a moment, by one event, and there's no going back. Without realizing it, they become adults before their time.

In 1971, Ethan grew up.

His friend Jason, his brother William Patrick and the late Derrick's sister Sarah also grew up that year.

That year Ethan realized the meaning of death. That year he experienced what it feels like when somebody you shared your life with dies and leaves you with no hope for another encounter, ever. And he learned just how big that remaining emptiness can be, a space that no one else can fill again.

The year of 1971 began, by the looks, as a promising one for Ethan and his friends. Everything going right, it should have continued that way. It lasted for one unforgettable summer, a filled up, happy childhood, and a promising youth that was just emerging. But 1971 turned into the year of death instead.

1970 news broadcasted the deaths of many celebrities, among them Jimi Hendrix and Janis Joplin, who fell victim to drug overdoses. 1971 brought more news of famous people's deaths to Greenfield. Louis Armstrong died on the sixth of July. Other more or less known celebrities also died. Thousands of unknown soldiers, youngsters, died, leaving their lives behind on the battlefields, in swamps and jungles of Vietnam. Women, children, old people and boys also died. killed by American boys.

And Derrick Zachariah died that year too.

Few deaths are expected. Many deaths occur suddenly, but they all come uninvited. Unwanted. When someone goes to war, the possibility they will never come back exists. When somebody kills, they put themselves in danger of being killed. And if someone is fourteen—with a life and future ahead of them, death doesn't fit into their course of life.

Derrick's death was a blow to the whole Greenfield and there was almost not a person who didn't attend his funeral to say the last unspoken word, utter a final farewell and shed a tear of remembrance.

On the day of Derrick's burial, life in Greenfield halted. Everybody who knew him and even those that did not came to the local cemetery. After they lowered Derrick's body into the grave and his casket saw the last, tiny part of the cloudy sky and falling rain, after everybody except the closest members of his family left the cemetery, the life reluctantly flowed back into Greenfield. It circulated slowly in its streets, fields and plains, coming back to its everyday routine.

But nothing was as it used to be.

Ethan's company fell apart.

Sarah Zachariah devoted herself to studying. She soothed her pain in the books and the knowledge she derived from them. She became the best student at school. Her behavior was exemplary. She took no part in fights anymore—there was nobody to fight for. She became quiet, withdrawn. Dignified too. She spent her free time in the house or near the house with her mother and father, staying close to her mother who shrank away day after day. Her heart couldn't put up with the loss of her son. Two years later, she joined Derrick. Her heart broke with the sorrow.

Sarah continued to look after her father who turned gray and became an old man almost overnight. But, despite that, he never gave up his vet's practice. Always ready to help others, even during the hardest moments of grief over the loss of his son and his wife. His personal tragedy helped him to learn the real value and greatness of life—the values he now appreciated even more.

Ben Zachariah drew his strength from life and his struggle for life. He helped himself by helping others, including Sarah. He knew the end would come should he yield. He couldn't give up. Not because of Sarah. Benjamin Zachariah knew, should anything happen to him, his brother Dan, who lived in Lincoln, would continue to support Sarah and help her finish her studies. But most of all he knew it was himself, Ben, Sarah needed. Just as he needed her. The death, that tore them apart from their beloved ones, forged a firm connection between father and daughter. Benjamin Zachariah didn't mean to let it break up ahead of time.

Jason Hawk. Jason kept company with the McCoy brothers for some time, but that became rarer. Eventually, he saw Ethan only in their class at school, while he met Will in the school's corridor, in town, and at his father's store where Will worked every day. He was saving the money for a trip he planned to take around the world. Or, Jason might see Will rafting down the river. Alone, absent-minded, with his look directed at nothing in particular. Then there was not even that. Will destroyed the raft one evening, breaking the last link connecting them and reminding them of their childhood.

Jason, with the help of his father who became so skilled with the farmed animals as if he had made his first steps on the pastures, devoted himself to horse breeding. He became an excellent rider and a master at throwing a lasso. The horses liked him, and he liked them. Had anybody told him, then, what he would do for a living later in his life, he would have had a good laugh. The truth was Jason's love for horses never faded away, though it was later reduced to occasional rides with the deafening thunder of the hoofs and the wind screaming in his hair.

Three and a half years after Derrick's death, Jim Hawk bought a big part of the pasture, including all the horses and the house from Ben Zachariah. That house was now his real home he longed after for so many years.

Yet another dream turned into reality.

Ethan and Will remained close despite all that happened. Although they didn't speak as much as they used to and their communication became sparser after their friend's death, Derrick's death made them closer.

The expression on Derrick's face, the image of the bridge, the river, the crowd of the people on the riverbank and his swollen, pale and distorted appearance wouldn't leave them either by day or by night. Derrick would slip into them like a remembrance during the day while haunting them in the nightmares during the nights. Especially Ethan.

Will would often hear Ethan's sobs and cries through the doorways of their rooms at night, which they kept open ever since Derrick's drowning. He would then jump out of his bed, run into Ethan's room and sit on the bed beside his brother.

One night, the sky was bright and exceptionally beautiful, tossing shadows over Ethan's face glimmering with tears.

"Hush, hush, calm down. That was just a dream. Everything's all right," Will said, embracing him, while he shivered out of control. "Everything's okay. It will go away. It's gone."

"It won't go away, it won't. It can't." He gasped for air between the sobs. "It's coming back again. Derrick's been here. . . ."

Then he started narrating.

The night was young; it was the twilight of an early fall day. Ethan, Derrick and Jason were returning from school. Halfway home, three local thugs intercepted them and started to bully them. Slightly drunk, two of them grabbed Jason and Ethan while the third one, a leader, pounced on Derrick. Encouraged by the laughter and the drunk cheering of his buddies, he kept poking Derrick in the stomach with the neck of his bottle. It didn't take him long before he became even more violent. He slapped Derrick once; he slapped him twice, just for kicks at first and then ever stronger and more serious. *Slap! Slap! Slap!*

Derrick looked at his friends through tears in his eyes, in a silent voice pleading for help. They stood there motionless and petrified with fear. The blow came knocking the glasses off Derrick's face and making him totter. Derrick's friends jumped in unison, startled by the sudden blast that resembled the sound of a nasty kid's play with the firecrackers on the quiet evening before the Fourth of July.

Ethan tried to help Derrick, but was stopped by the firm grip and paralyzing pain that flashed through his neck. Jason tried to call for help but, as it always happens in the moments of fear too great for him to control it, he stammered. At last, with a great effort he stuttered a word which mingled with a moan from Derrick's throat.

"Ssssherrifffff!"

Threatening the three little friends with their fists, the thugs ran away just when the sheriff's car drove past them.

Derrick pulled himself together and picked up his glasses. He put them on and looked at his friends through the broken glass. He said something that froze the blood in Ethan's veins.

In a voice as calm as the descending night, he spoke words as icy as the water of the January River in which Derrick, his belly up, floated at that moment.

"Why did you let that happen? Why didn't you *help* me?"

His voice, distant and cold, echoed in Ethan's head as he shook it from side to side, his eyes closed. When he opened them again, Derrick didn't float in the river that took his life away, but was now in his room, right beside Ethan's bed. He bled from his nostrils and his ears, and he looked even more ghastly in the pale moonlight than when his body was pulled out from the river. He spoke nothing, he just moved his lips. The words came out from his mouth in a slow motion, yet they exploded with a loud *bang!* in Ethan's head.

"Why-did-you-let-that-happen-to-me? I-thought-we-were-friends. . . ."

At that moment, Ethan woke up.

That was just a dream, one of many, in which Ethan's consciousness came to Derrick's ghost begging for forgiveness. Forgiveness for being alive while his friend's body rested in the dark chambers of pale memories.

It was just another dream, one of many, after which Will came to his room, sat beside him and consoled him. That particular night he also sat on Ethan's bed until Ethan regained his composure, talking to him in a calm and soothing voice. "But, Et, that was a long time ago. That incident after the school. A lot happened since then and I'm sure Derrick forgave you and forgot about the whole thing long ago. Don't fret yourself with that anymore."

He wanted to encourage him. He wanted to make the spooks go away, but the vision of Derrick which Ethan's subconsciousness turned into a ghost and directed the end of a past event startled him too.

"We didn't help him, Willy." Ethan was not to be mollified. "We didn't save him. That's why he's dead now." He lost his composure again. "That's why he's gone. Derrick . . . Derrick, I'm so sorry. . . ."

Will kept quiet. He left it to the passing minutes to do their job, to separate reality from the past and the bad dreams. He left it to the night to uncover the picture of his brother's future before his own eyes, while covering the past with a veil of condolence, forgiveness and nice memories of their mutual friend.

As Ethan's breathing steadied, he spoke again. But now he talked about other things. He talked about events and days which had nothing to do with the death that had left such a mark in their lives. He talked about people and adventures which didn't call for condolence, but were tickling the merry disposition and urging the laughter. William Patrick tried to make his brother laugh (as he did before, in the many nights preceding this one) and he succeeded. They went on talking and talking until the break of dawn and only then they parted, each leaving for their respective bed before their parents discovered and caught them in the act. The next day they roamed drowsy through the house, smiling at their mother's remarks about them looking as if they hadn't slept a wink last night, but readily followed their father when the time came for them to go into a wheat field. The wheat sowing was in full swing.

Will and Riv were those who helped Ethan get over the months of crisis. And then Will was gone, and so was Riv after a couple of months. Will, who served his country, couldn't come home to be by his brother's side. And it was then when Ethan needed him most.

River's death was a severe blow to Ethan. It left his world in a heap of ruins. It also left the poisoned River's body with a small sheet of paper attached to it:

THAT'S WHAT HAPPENS TO DOG THIEVES

Warren Preston waited for his revenge for almost three and a half years. Three and a half years dawned with the moment of revenge. And, as it usually happens, at the worst time.

Ethan didn't know whether it was Warren who had done that himself or was it a deed of some of his pals or a few of them. It didn't matter. Ethan knew Warren was behind that incident, and that was all that mattered.

In the backyard of the McCoy home, under the sky screaming with countless shades of the red color of the setting sun, the body of his four-legged friend lay next to the white wicker chair of the courtyard suite of furniture, his head facing the stairs that lead to the kitchen. On weak legs, his body shaking with spasms and the bloody foam sticking together his beautiful golden hair, January River dragged himself with his last strength toward the rescuing threshold. A note with the ominous message written by a juvenile hand, but with sharp and determined lines, was attached to the collar hidden under the thick hair. It clung to it resisting weaker and weaker moves of the dog's head, as if it did not want to part with it before it fulfills its mission. He needed only a few more breaths and a little strength for another whine to call his friend whose laughter he could hear from an open kitchen door. January River had no strength for that. He lay on a soft grass looking at the open door in expectation and hope. He kept looking like that even when Ethan came out into the backyard, jumping over the stairs and halting. Petrified. Except, there was no life in the eyes of January River any longer. The look of empty and lifeless eyes merged with Ethan's look and remained there. January River, the favorite of the McCoys and their friends, died alone. Listening to the laughter of the boy who saved him on the bank of the frozen river, the laughter of a friend he would die for. This was the sound he liked to hear most. That dear sound got more distant, becoming weaker and weaker while he lost consciousness and the agony that contracted his body died away.

Months later, when Ethan turned in vain in the direction of the river, the fields, the cottonwood forest, the pines, and the bare branches of the deciduous trees, hoping to hear the familiar bark and spot the running of the dog that wasn't there, when he passed by the empty dog's dish which contained no remnants of food, none of it made a difference. The only important thing was the memory of Riv, his best friend, and Ethan promised himself to do everything in his power to keep the memories from fading away. He wouldn't let the best part of his life die. Ever.

He took down all the maps of the universe, the photographs of comets and galaxies collected from *National Geographic* and other journals from the green walls of his room. He redecorated them with the photographs and drawings of River he drew from memory. The only two photos that remained were a picture of himself at eight and Will, ten, along with the photo of them with River their father took a year ago. Everything else had been removed, and he now devoted this space to the memory of River.

The short telephone conversations and the letters from Will in which he encouraged his brother and boosted his morale trying to bring back purpose and joy into his life all seemed useless and futile. Ethan was always happy to hear Will's voice, but—to Will—he seemed absentminded and restrained. That wasn't the real Ethan. At least, not the one he said goodbye to when leaving.

Will didn't know how to help him, and he fretted himself about that. He learned from his parents that Ethan had dug himself into the library and was leaving it only when he had to obey the call of nature or when they had to close it. Not even the humor, Ethan's parents tried to cheer him up with, worked with Ethan. Withdrawing into his shell, he only accepted the company of the books in whose pages he buried himself.

He would come home with a new book each day, and then he would read it late into the night until he finished the last page. Thus, in the year while Will was away in the army, Ethan read Capote's *In Cold Blood* four times. Ira McCoy learned that from Mrs. Kozlowski, who worked in the library. Mrs. Kozlowski rang up Ethan's mother to praise her son's interest for the literature, but also expressed her concern about the dark stuff Ethan always borrowed.

Mrs. Kozlowski couldn't know that in the disasters of the people he read about—in this case, the Clutter family from Holcomb whose murderers, Richard Hickock and Perry Smith, Ethan also considered to be victims of the millstones of life— Ethan found sympathy and the way out of his own sorrow. Neither Mrs. Kozlowski, his mother nor anybody else knew Ethan drew strength from his escape into the lives of literary characters, who rose like a phoenix from the ashes of their personal tragedies. For his tragedy was nothing smaller than tragedies of the people he read about.

Now, when Will and River were no longer there, *In Cold Blood* became his closest companion. Ethan built up a special closeness with the incident that shook and flabbergasted the whole of America fourteen years ago and brought it to a new life in his hands. For Ethan, *In Cold Blood* was the best book he read in many years, and, should somebody secretly peek into his heart, they wouldn't be surprised to find out it remained the same one he was most fond of.

In Cold Blood was Ethan's ticket to the world of literature.

The outcome of many books he read and the worried talks between Ira McCoy and Natalie Kozlowski was the world that opened itself up before Ethan. The world that reached far beyond the borders of Greenfield, the whole new land of make-believe. Yet another consequence, which didn't please Ethan in the least, but which was logical, was his shortsightedness. He hardly got used to wearing glasses (to which he puffed disapprovingly), yet he accepted them as a necessary evil. If he wanted to read on, he had to get used to them. That was the only reason why he accepted them.

Ethan didn't notice how quickly the days without Will passed by. One day a familiar figure just popped up at his room's door. A little older, tanned, but stronger still and even more handsome. Ethan dropped Uris' *Battle Cry* on his bed and hurried into his brother's hug.

"You got taller, bro," Will observed. "You are more serious and good-looking too. These glasses must be credited for that." He took them off Ethan's nose and put them on. "What do you think? How do I look with them?"

"Awful!" Ethan laughed and took them back.

Will told about his adventures in the military, and Ethan relaxed in his presence. He started feeling like the old Ethan. Unbelievable how much Will's return meant to him. Soon he changed so much that—influenced by the stories of the Marine Corps that he could only read about until now—he could hardly wait to serve Uncle Sam and get out of Greenfield. The pressure he felt became more difficult to bear, and Will managed just slightly to ease it. The pressure of fretting and remembering which placed a burden on him kept getting heavier to carry around.

When the time came for Ethan to leave Greenfield, he soon realized that not everything in the military fit Will's description. Ethan knew why Will didn't tell him about that other, uglier side he had to learn about in person. He would have to face it sooner or later, so Will didn't want to discourage him in advance with things he couldn't change anyway. And when Ethan came back home, not only did he look discouraged, but he was also about thirty pounds lighter.

Will wasn't in Greenfield anymore. He moved to New York City. Before he found his own place to live in, he stayed with his friend Donald with whom he served in the army. He got a job as a waiter in a restaurant in Manhattan where he awaited the fulfillment of his dream: to embark on a ship and take a voyage around the world.

Will's decision hit his parents hard. They didn't fancy it, let alone approve of it. Unlike them, Ethan knew his brother was getting closer to fulfilling his dreams. Though he was cross with him for not waiting for him to return from the army, Ethan shared his feelings with Will. Will didn't know his younger brother was with him with all his heart.

They were on their own now. They were adults. They became men. For a twinkle of time they missed the taste of Vietnam and joined the army. At the dawn of the Watergate scandal they returned to their homes. Soon they would have their own families and careers. That's how it is in life.

The future was before them. With all the responsibilities that come with the package.

What Ethan didn't know then was where his future would take him and what it would bring.

11

The sun set on the Manhattan skyline, disappearing behind its skyscrapers, its glow replaced with artificial illumination. The falling night, rich in sounds, was pleasant and refreshing. The air resounded with shouting, laughing kids running down the street, garbage collectors banging metal trash cans as they emptied them into the back of the truck, the noise of traffic mixed with ships on the East River announcing their arrival in the harbor accompanied by the cries of seagulls.

Ethan was now familiar with that voice of New York City in which he had lived for seven years already. He'd gotten used to The Big Apple and grown fond of it. Kind of like an orphan to his foster-mother's singing to him softly before bedtime, or a stray dog doomed to its world of freedom, solitude and an occasional scrap of food. But Ethan missed many things in Greenfield. Most of all the smell of cut grass and dried hay, as well as the smell of freshly reaped wheat. He remembered his boyhood days when he had no worries on his mind except that the truth about aliens would leak out one day, and what a good feeling it was to bury your arms up to your elbows in the whiteness of fresh flour. He longed for the times when he played in the fields choked with rustling corn. The freedom of the vast space cradled in the arms of the countryside. And for tender whispers of the soft wind along with the endless wisdom of an ancient sky. He missed being a child. A carefree, happy child.

For Ethan, and any resident of Greenfield, there wasn't a nicer place on the face of the earth. Endless high plains intersected by streams emptying into the Missouri River, shaped it into plateaus and uplands toward the West and rose into rocks and snowy peaks of the Rocky Mountains in the far distance. The north winds blew over abundant plateaus of plowed fields suited for the cultivation of wheat, corn, rye, barley, beans, and sugar beets. Intermingled with pastures and loess plains they brought the scent and freshness of the Great Lakes, along with rains and snowstorms producing low temperatures in the winter. Summer storms and tornadoes were not unusual there. Fortunately, none of the present residents of Greenfield lived there when the last, deadly twister struck. The sky above Greenfield still had the innocent, blue color, which, as the day drew to an end, would portray yet another of its unforgettable sunsets.

Splashing the banks, the January River flowed nearby, irrigating the nearby plowlands via a system of canals increasing their fertility. The channels ran into the North Platte prior to joining their sister, the South Platte. Finally, all three converged with the Platte River.

The January River, favorite of all inhabitants of Greenfield, gave not only life, but provided desired relief from the hot, dry summer months. It possessed a special beauty of its own, even though it was not navigable like the Mississippi on which boats and steamships traveled. Nor was it strange and mysterious like the Amazon or wild, dangerous and untamable like the Colorado. But it was a part of Greenfield and its inhabitants, and that accounted for its special meaning and beauty. If Greenfield was renowned for anything save its first-class flour, cereals, corn, barley, high-class cattle, wonderful people, and beautiful landscapes, it was for the January River.

However, for Ethan McCoy, Greenfield meant more than just a river. For Ethan McCoy, it stood for more than the birthplace where he spent his childhood and more than half his life that he now nostalgically reminisced. More than the reality and memories he accumulated during his life there. Far more than what could happen to an ordinary man in a lifetime.

As the days went by and time healed wounds, Ethan's memories faded, losing their authenticity and viability. In the hubbub of New York City, the silence and tranquility of Greenfield slipped further away until Ethan had to consciously fight to recall them. Confronted with a different world and a new way of life, they seemed increasingly more plastic and surreal to him as he breathed in the foul stench of relentless cruelty and rawness, almost feeling the tragedy of promised hopes and shattered dreams. This new reality was *his* reality, engulfed with images of frantic people running somewhere with the last rays of dusk followed by the sounds of distant gunshots (which always happened to someone else), accompanied by screams of spilled and spoiled blood. Though he hadn't quite become fond of it, he had accepted it as a part of his new life. His new environment. Inevitable, no matter how he tried to pretend otherwise. When he attempted to run away from it, to escape, it proved to be pointless. He found the same around every damn corner. So, he switched. He changed his life philosophy. He stopped running and learned to adapt.

As Ethan stood at the window of Will's apartment, he watched the city waking up. Its bright lights under the veil of dark-blue and, within the next thirty minutes, an even darker late afternoon. He scanned the skyline, taking in the buildings of the Watchtower Society with a large inscription glaring on its turret-like top. Over to South Street Seaport and almost reaching City Hall, stood the hundred-and-four-year-old Brooklyn Bridge—a faithful sentinel connecting the Brooklyn district with Downtown Manhattan. Northwest of it, projected the Empire State Building, the second highest in the city (third, if one were honest). Directly south, the World Trade Center towered over all the others. Dominating the highest points in New York City, the Twins were surrounded by smaller skyscrapers of beautiful steel and glass.

Further south nestled three smaller islands—Governors, Ellis and Liberty Islands. On the last one stood a lady that came all the way from Paris to welcome her new children, the Statue of Liberty. With the thoughtful and warning look it promised them nothing, but hard work and uncertainty, but also the revelation of hidden treasures in the Promise Land. Never failing in her mission, she welcomed millions of people throughout the years who came to the United States of America searching for a new beginning. Seven years ago, she had done the same for Ethan.

Looking at the lights of the big city, Ethan tried to remember how he enjoyed watching the illuminated Greenfield from his clearing in the woods.

Many a time he stood on the banks of the East River, listening to the splashes and nervous rush of its water. That was when he recalled the sounds of the January River best.

Recollection upon recollection, time and again he returned to the past. When he parted from Peter, with whom he had just finished checking paperwork in what now had become his mill. Heading home for supper, he had just enough time to take a quick shower and change before his mother brought food to the table. Even after seventeen years (from what Ethan remembered) the habit of saying grace and reading the Bible hadn't changed in the McCoy family. Only then did Sean, Ira, and their sons allow themselves to eat supper.

"A letter from Will came today," Sean McCoy said, when they finished the meal and the table cleared. Ira McCoy washed the dishes in the kitchen.

"Yes? What does it say? Where is he now?"

"Don't know. Didn't open it. It's addressed to you."

"To me?"

"Mailed from Canada." Father handed the letter to Ethan.

While Ethan opened the envelope and read the letter, Sean McCoy occupied himself with his pipe.

"He sends his regards and says he loves you." Ethan

refolded the letter, stuffed it back into the envelope. "They've discharged the load in Quebec and he's coming back to New York. Maybe he's already there."

"Does he say anything else?"

"He does." Ethan looked at his father's face through the small clouds of smoke. "He'll stay ashore for two weeks and invited me to come visit him in New York."

"Will you go?" his father asked.

"I don't know. I haven't had time to consider that."

"Would you like to go?" Sean McCoy said after a short pause.

Ethan looked at the thirty-five-years-older man, thinking how to respond. Should he lie or be frank with him? Should he admit that he was fed up with Greenfield, with the mill, wheat, corn and the barley, that he was ready to give up the ghosts of the past as well as the anemic present? And confess that he needed a change? Should he say aloud he longed for the real, hard work, something he could create with his own hands, through his own pain, by the sweat of his brow, and he longed to taste the life outside the borders of Greenfield? Should he kill his dreams or inflict a pain upon his father, like Will did and go his own way? Be independent?

Ethan knew their ways would inevitably part someday. He would eventually leave Greenfield. The question was whether to do it the way Will had—to travel the world during his youth to return to his hearth later—or to leave for good, with no possibility of return and no nostalgia. That's what Ethan was afraid of, and why he hadn't pondered leaving. At twenty-two, he still had enough time before him to think it over and decide where to build his tomorrow.

This explained why Will's letter shook him more than he cared to show his father. Alarm bells rang in his mind, along with the blaring siren announcing the ship's departure from the harbor. So, what stopped him? Only that Ethan had no way of knowing if he were to jump aboard and leave and whether he would ever return.

"I don't know," he answered, as vaguely as possible. "Maybe I would. In that case I could talk to Peter to take over the business of running the mill while I'm gone. I must think it over, anyway. This has popped up quite suddenly."

"Big decisions are often made suddenly. The biggest deals are made in a fraction of a second. It's up to our wisdom, wits and shrewdness whether they will be worth the trouble or boomerang and hit us in the head."

"Father, you know all too well that Will always dreamed of sailing the seas."

"It's not Will I'm talking about, Ethan." His father looked straight into the blueness of his eyes. "I'm talking about life. And the possibilities it provides. But also the responsibilities it brings. To ourselves and others. No man's an individual. He's a part of society. Thus, the consequences of our deeds don't only influence ourselves on a personal level, they affect those connected to us."

"Father," Ethan now felt compelled to ask the question he tried to avoid, "what do you think? Should I go visit Will? Even for a short while?"

"I think you're a mature, responsible and smart boy capable of making his own decisions. Plus, you've got a good foundation. You've been brought up well and you had a good education. You must make your own decisions in accordance with all that. The decisions of lesser importance as well as those that will affect your future. And then you will have to stand up for them and be prepared to take the consequences. Remember how God gave Israelites the choice between blessing and damnation? They could not have chosen both or none."

Sean McCoy wished him good night and went to bed.

Ethan remained sitting for a while longer, turning Will's letter over and over in his hand. He read it once again in peace, went to bid goodnight to his mother, and then retreated to his room.

Ten days later he ended up in New York City.

He got off the Amtrak train at Penn Station where Will

waited for him. Ethan experienced a jolt he'd rarely, if ever, felt before. As the brothers pushed their way through the station hall, Ethan—without being aware of doing it— tightened the grip on his traveling bag and kept it closer to his leg. He felt minuscule and unprotected, thinking he could get lost if he turned around for even a second, although Will was beside him the entire time.

They left Penn Station and took a cab. Will explained it would have been much quicker if they took the subway, but he wanted his brother to see the city.

"How do you like it?" he asked, as they rode down Broadway, with the Empire State Building rising behind them.

"What?"

"Christ, Ethan, where do you think we are? New York. Manhattan. The Big Apple."

"Ugh, it's big. But rather impressive." He tried to catch sight of the tops of the skyscrapers, close and far as they went by them. They almost reached the metallic-blue sky.

"You're sure right about that. Just wait until you see Downtown and Lower Manhattan. Then you'll talk about bigness."

Passing Union Square, they continued to glide down Broadway. Stuck in the gridlock, not hurrying anywhere. Ethan was overwhelmed with impressions. The mass of people hurrying up and down the streets reminded Ethan of bugs roaming aimlessly about, though he knew each one had its destination and purpose. Some wore stern looks on their faces, while others smiled and nonchalantly held hands. (Ethan was stunned to see two guys holding hands and hugging while crossing the street. Though surprised and confused, he didn't get a chance to mention it to his brother). Others were dressed in dark Armani, Versace and Yves Saint Laurent business suits and chewed gum. Ethan also noticed casually dressed people. With the traffic so dense, Ethan wondered how the city functioned at all. Several times yellow cabs flashed up in front of them, swerved to the curb for a quick stop to pick up a passenger, and then eased back into traffic. With his eyes wide and mouth open, Ethan admired their stunts. His mind full of impressions, he paid no attention to what Will was telling him.

"Ethan!"

"What?" he jumped, startled.

"Something wrong?"

"No, everything's fine. Why?"

"Come on, let me have it. I know something's bothering you."

"Nothing's bothering me. I'm just trying to understand this city."

"Ethan, I know you too well. Remember, I'm your bro, you cannot fool me. It's not just the city, right?"

"No, it's not. You're right."

"So, what's the problem?"

"Mum. And Dad." He sighed. "I've been thinking of them."

"There's a word for that. Nostalgia," Will said in a melancholic way. "I know the feeling. It'll go away."

"It's not nostalgia. I'd say it's more like guilt. Or something close to it."

"Guilt?" Will unintentionally raised his voice. "Why guilt?"

"I believe they expected me to stay in Greenfield."

"Yes? And what did you expect? What you expect from life isn't that important anymore?"

"Will, how can you say that?"

"Sorry, pal. That's not what I meant. Et, I love Mum and Dad just like you do. I wouldn't have achieved anything without them. And I wouldn't have made it to New York."

As their taxi moved along after a few minutes, the Tweed Courthouse and municipal building behind it came into view. Seconds later, the Brooklyn Bridge appeared through the haze.

Will continued, "But you've got to understand one thing. I'm not a child. *We* are not children anymore. We have our own lives, and it's our right to decide how to live them. Our parents may or may not agree with our decisions. But that's always been the case, and yet they always got over it. Well, maybe not completely, but they put up with it. You know what I mean."

"I know, Will, but I don't want to hurt them. I don't want to cause them pain. I don't want to let them down."

"You'll disappoint them only if you disappoint yourself. If you are unhappy. There's nothing worse for parents than when their child is unhappy and suffers. Got that?"

"You're probably right."

"Then get rid of that sour expression on your face and start absorbing the world around you."

They paused on Cranberry Street, not too far from the Watchtower buildings. A nearby sign disclosed the message: READ GOD'S WORD, THE HOLY BIBLE, DAILY. Will paid the cabbie and then the two brothers entered the four-story building where Will lived. In contrast to the skyscrapers that populated Manhattan, Ethan found this building more welcoming. He felt more natural, more normal and down to earth.

Will's apartment was simple, clean and economical. The living room was separated from the kitchen by a small bar. A wooden staircase led to the upper floor, to a bedroom with a large double bed. Next to the living room was a bathroom, with a tub and a toilet, plus a small storage room. The apartment was bright and sunny, it felt warm, and Ethan liked it.

"I didn't know you were living in the attic," he commented.

"Actually, they call it a loft. But I know what you mean; it feels like an attic. Are you disappointed I'm not living in a sky-scraper?"

"No, no. On the contrary! I like this. I'd feel claustrophobic in one of those buildings. This is much better."

"You don't seem too impressed?"

"Excuse me?"

"I was thinking of New York. You don't seem so enthusi-astic about it."

"Oh no. I just got here. I need a little time to get used to everything, that's all. The skyscrapers are nice to look at, but I'm not sure I'd like to stay in one, even though some of them must be quite luxurious."

"You would be surprised how much people pay to live in

them. To be honest, they are worth the price."

"They better be. But not for me, as I already said."

"We can go sightseeing later if you want. The view from the Empire State and World Trade Center is worth every bit of the effort. Knowing you, I think you'd love it."

"Okay. But first I would like to take a shower. Can I use the bathroom?"

"Don't act like a damn tourist. Go ahead. Make yourself at home."

"Thanks."

Though he couldn't quite explain it to himself, Ethan felt that tight feeling in his chest again.

12

A week passed. Ethan and Will called their parents in Greenfield again to make sure everything was fine. Their father said everything ran normally; there was a minor halt in production at the mill, but Peter fixed the problem quickly. Everything was in order as far as the mill was concerned. Mother and he were well, thanks for asking. Ethan told them he liked it in New York and that he could find his way around the city without Will helping him. He also said he planned to stay, but couldn't say for how long when Sean asked him.

Then Will took over the phone and talked first to his mother and then to his father. He explained he had to sail to Southampton the day after tomorrow and that Ethan would be on his own for a while. No problem, he assured their worried mother, Ethan knew his way about the city, although he still got lost in the subway from time to time. But he'd soon learn his way in the underground too—Will had used the double meaning of the word on purpose and laughed at her excited reaction. After all, Mrs. Bates, the good soul of their landlady would gladly come to the rescue should Ethan need something. No reason for them to worry.

He wished them all well, sent his love and hung up.

"What do you think, how long should I stay?" Ethan asked. "And what will I be doing while you're away sailing the seas?"

"Stay for as long as you like. We told our parents you wouldn't be coming home for a while. Make use of the apartment since I have to pay the rent for it."

"That's okay, but what will I *do*?"

"What will you do? In New York, you can do lots of things. Have fun. Go sightseeing. Weeks won't be enough for you to go around and see all this city offers. Go to the movies. See the shows on Broadway or cheer for the Yankees." He laughed at the expression on his brother's face. "Okay, that was a bad suggestion, but you can still visit museums, bookstores and libraries. Once you get inside The New York Public Library on Fifth and begin to rummage through its books, you won't be out of there before you're an old man. Central Park is also beautiful at this time of the year. A real pleasure. But I warn you, don't go there at night, unless you want to try out how it feels to get robbed or experience sex with a guy or even more than one. The same goes for the Bronx."

"Ha, ha, very funny."

"It isn't funny. That's why I'm warning you. There are lots of things you can see, do or visit here. You okay for money? I can leave you some cash, if you need it."

"The money isn't the issue. At least not now."

"Fine, then. As you might have observed already, the nightlife in New York is also rich. This is the city that never sleeps, and some places are open around the clock. There's no problem with the call girls, either. You can get one whenever you wish. Spending the night shouldn't be a problem for such a handsome boy."

"You're joking, right?"

"That's New York, bro. Everything I said is true. It's up to you what to choose how to spend your time here."

"I think there are better ways of spending one's time than inspecting the nightclubs."

"I don't doubt that." Will smiled. "Still a puritan? True to yourself for life."

"Call it what you like. I came here because of you. Because you invited me. Not to rot in some bar."

"That's perfectly okay. Nice of you. But now I'm moving on, and you've been here too short a time to go back home. You've only just arrived. Is there anything special I can help you with while I'm still here?"

Ethan paused for a moment and then said, "Perhaps. But I don't know whether you can help me with that or not."

His mysteriousness intrigued Will. "I'm listening. Try me."

"I'd like to work."

William Patrick grinned. "What I listed wasn't enough for you?"

"I'm afraid you didn't get it. I want a *job*."

"You mean . . . ?" Will's voice sang with incredulity.

"Yes, a paid job. I'll take any job for a newcomer we can find. So, I can brag later that I worked in the biggest apple of the world."

Will laughed and answered, "No problem."

"What do you mean, no problem?"

"If you want to work, we'll find you a job." Will tried to hide a smile as Ethan got even more confused. "Have you made up your mind?"

"Wait, hold on a second. Are you trying to say you can find me a job?"

"Et, what do you think I've been doing in New York these past years? Twiddling my thumbs, sittin' on the docks, and waiting for somebody to take pity on me? I was working, Ethan. Making money. Not the big money, but money nonetheless. Time is money here and the sooner you accept that, the better for you. I lived on the money I earned and in the moments of crisis I helped myself with savings I earned back home until the moment I waited for didn't come. I moved around too, making acquaintances. I got to know people who introduced me to other people. That's how it works here. I must admit I got to know all sorts of scum, but enough nice people as well. I'd like to introduce you to some of them, if you haven't changed your mind. But we better hurry. We don't have a lot of time."

"Those people would hire me? With no recommendations, a total stranger?"

"And what about me? I'm nothing? My word is not good enough?"

"I didn't mean that. It's just I'm not sure they're running around the streets looking for workers."

"I'm not, either. But it's worth a try. We have nothing to lose."

"*You* have nothing to lose. I have a mill to run which I'd have to quit."

"Just for a while, Ethan."

"It doesn't matter. If Father goes nuts, it might be for good."

"He won't go nuts. I'll talk to him if that's what bothers you. I'm not afraid of him."

"I didn't say I'm afraid of him. The thing is, I don't know if I can do that to him. He gave me that mill. He signed all the papers and put it in my name. Should I express my appreciation for what he did by saying, *Thank you, Father, I'm returning the mill to you, I found a better job*?"

"Nobody said anything about returning the mill. Did I mention that?"

"But what are my options? What should we do with the mill, then? *Sell* it?"

"I don't understand how you cannot put two and two together! Don't you see the obvious? The mill remains yours. There's no need for you to sell it or give it back to Dad. It stays yours. Got that part? Don't sell it and don't give it back to Dad."

"Yeah, I got that. It's easy for you to say. But did you think about one little thing and that is who'll run the mill if I pack my bags and go?"

"And who's running it now?"

"Well, Peter is running it, but. . . ."

Will smiled.

"Are you trying to say—"

"Yes. Thank, heavens, my little brother finally got a grasp of it. That's what I'm trying to say to you. Let Peter run the mill. Give him a raise and let him take over your part of the job. I hear he's very good. What's even more important, you can trust the guy."

"Well, yes, but. . . ."

"What? What now? You said you wanted a job here. You want it, or are you trying to piss me off?"

"I can't believe I'm doing this. I can't believe I'm even *think-ing* about something like that."

"And what were you thinking when you decided to come up here? Were you thinking about making a career in the mill in Nebraska in the middle of nowhere?"

"That's a low blow and you know it. You know what I was thinking about." Ethan said, feeling affronted. "I was thinking about you and your call. I wanted to see *you*, I wanted to see where you lived and how you were doing. We haven't been to-gether for years. I see you only for holidays and that's it. Do you think I don't miss you? Did you think I didn't miss your com-pany? Did you think I didn't miss you *all that time*?"

There were also other reasons Ethan thought about before he decided to come to New York, but he didn't say anything about them to William. It would be out of place to do that now, anyway.

Prompted by his brother's candor and the outburst of his feelings, William also opened his heart and said in a reconcilia-tory manner: "I missed you too, Et. In each harbor we docked, I thought of you and I was sorry you weren't with me. I wished I could just reach out my hand, grab you and show you what a great place the world is. I wished you could see the things I saw, smell the smells I smelled and meet the people I met, and enjoy every bit the way I did. That's why I'm so glad you came to New York. You've at least made it up to here. And I want you to take a full advantage of this trip and remember it by doing something nice. I don't want it to be that the two of us saw each other for a few days and then we parted again. I want to *do* something for you. I can do something for my brother, can't I?"

Ethan looked at Will's sneakers, his head lowered. Will moved a step forward and put his hands on his shoulders.

"Kiddo, I want you to grab this opportunity. Who knows when the next one will come? How many times does one get a chance of a lifetime? And we must fight even for that one. But you don't have to. I made a breakthrough for both of us. You only have to say yes and seize what I offered you with both hands. If you want it, that is. If you *really* want to taste the life outside Greenfield."

Ethan raised his head and looked into his brother's eyes.

"Well, bro? What are we gonna do?" Will asked.

"I think I'll go for it."

"That's it, old buddy!" Will embraced him. "That's what I call the spirit. That's my baby brother."

"It seems so," Ethan beamed, feeling relieved. When he made the decision, he got a heavy burden off his chest.

"Where could I work? Do you have something on your mind?"

Will nodded.

"You may like it at Sebastian's. That's where I got the job when I first came to New York. It was at Sebastian's that I lived for the day when I finally embarked on *The Nightingale*. This restaurant brings luck. It brought it to me, and I hope the same will happen to you."

"If I won't be like a bull in a china shop and demolish it before or maybe even poison someone."

"Don't worry, the costs will be deducted from your salary. And know the salary is quite a good one, so you'll be able to afford a piece of roguery from time to time."

"Don't jump to conclusions. We'll see about that."

"If we have agreed on everything, we could have a snack now. My stomach is demanding its rights." He patted his belly.

"The same goes for me, now that you've mentioned it. Where are we going to eat? What shall I put on?"

"You can guess twice."

"What?! No, you're kidding me. You cannot do that. I'm not ready yet. Besides, my tie is all wrinkled up." Ethan panicked.

"I'll give you mine," Will laughed. "But you don't have to put it on. The owner isn't keen on formalities."

"He may not be, but I am! We are talking about New York here, formalities or not. The last thing I need is to lose a job because of a tie."

Will roared with laughter.

That afternoon Ethan visited Sebastian's as a customer.

Two days later he started working there as a waiter.

13

When Ethan returned to reality, supper was ready. The bell on the microwave gave a ring and Ethan switched it off to prevent the roast from getting too dried out. As the smell from the stove tickled his palate and spread through the apartment, Ethan continued to recall his first working day at Sebastian's.

Situated on West 57th Street, the restaurant Sebastian's was owned and run by Jeffrey Collins, who named it after his nine-year-old son. A few artistic photos of a smiling boy decorated the restaurant's walls. The boy's taste also dictated its menu.

Sebastian Collins was a great lover and advocate for animals, and he couldn't stand any harm or evil done to any of them. Sebastian considered eating animal flesh an act of barbarism, and he called the people he saw wolfing juicy steaks cruel and primitive. A witty caterer, Jeffrey Collins changed Sebastian's menu to vegetarian. The necessity of booking one's table in advance was a testament to his savvy business idea, especially when it came to planning business dinners. Jeffrey Collins' restaurant was always so crowded, it seemed as if half of the Manhattan population had turned into vegetarians overnight, or that animal protection activists nationwide got the word and had headed into town.

Sebastian's offered the whole spectrum of cooked, fried, stuffed, roasted, marinated and beautifully decorated vegetables as well as various puddings, salads and stewed vegetables, but the specialty of the house was the pancakes. Made in all possible and impossible ways. Jeffrey Collins also had a couple of recipes up his sleeve, which he kept as carefully guarded secrets. The good father fulfilled yet another whim of his child's who was ready to die from consuming excessive quantities of pancakes. And there was no reason why he shouldn't as they were quite popular and brought him a good profit.

Besides the pancakes, Sebastian's also offered a wide assortment of other cakes and cookies, many of which contained no eggs or milk. Of these Ethan loved blueberry pie the best. The menu also listed a wide variety of refreshing drinks and beverages, all alcohol free.

All in all, Sebastian's was a cozy, clean, tidy and a bit romantic restaurant. The politeness, attractiveness and likable ways of its owner helped its popularity, as well as the quality of the staff.

Ethan found his place in that "children's" restaurant under New York's sun.

Judging from his performance at work on the first evening, Ethan feared it would be his last dinner. He had butterflies in his stomach, his palms were sweating, and he kept dropping things. To his surprise, Jeffrey commended him at the end of the shift, saying he did satisfactory work for his first day.

Satisfactory? Ethan had to laugh at how his clumsiness had produced a compliment and been condoned. By his own judgment, he wasn't remotely good, but he still got another chance. He made much better use of his time the next day, and Jeffrey Collins confirmed that with a contented smile. Ethan soon became so natural and nimble on the job he surprised himself. Amazed at how the waiter's job was becoming to him. And how much he liked it.

Ethan also grew accustomed to the running which exhausted him in the beginning, to the pain in his back from excessive standing, to the sudden changes in orders, and to the whims of the customers. None of which was a problem for him now.

Ethan soon fit into the bloodstream of Sebastian's, just as Will said he would. As his brother had several years before him, Ethan became one of the most popular waiters. The demand at his tables didn't sag even when the rush of customers subsided. Ethan McCoy always had his hands full—either with work, or with plates.

Ethan could talk about many occasions and experiences he had while working at Sebastian's. But the most significant and life-altering experience happened at the business dinner for the editorial staff of the magazine *A Way of Life*.

At the end of every business year, its editorial board threw a party for the personnel at Sebastian's. One of those events when the restaurant was booked and closed to the public. That occasion was hectic as the workers strived to satisfy all the customers—many of whom had been faithful clients for many years.

Throughout the entire year the editorship kept their noses to the grindstone. With no time to rest on laurels, they changed the look of the magazine (for the upcoming year), made improvements in the quality of the print and paper, as well as to the topicality and novelty of each edition. Already under way with the goal to be completed before the year was out.

A Way of Life was a magazine for the whole family whose main topic changed every year. The last year's articles focused on how to improve the quality of life for a modern man with the nutrition issue to be replaced with the stories and surveys about the places and summer resorts all over the United States—attractive, acceptable and accessible for an average American family to vacation. The opinion survey by the journalists and contributors to *A Way of Life* showed Americans had above average interest for planning their next-year's vacations. As always, *A Way of Life* was set to fulfill what its readers expected.

In addition to the topics interesting for the whole family, *A Way of Life* also had sections for individual interests that covered the cultural life and the world of entertainment such as movies, theaters, concerts, museums, music, news from Hollywood and the film industry. As well as current trends in fiction, including a list of the ten best-selling books from the previous month. Interviews with celebrities—and those who were yet-to-become—could also be found there, and even sections on sports and politics for those fans. Although *A Way of Life* was an apolitical magazine, it provided unbiased news about significant political events in the United States and worldwide.

Under the editorial leadership of its owner, Susan Dupie, *A Way of Life* boldly made its way to an even greater number of readers. Soon it became one of the most popular magazines in the United States (especially in eastern parts). Its perspective was bright for the most part providing a professional mishap didn't occur, followed by a financial crash. However, that was unlikely since the magazine had a good financial background. If it came to that, Susan's father, Marc Dupie, would be ready to come to the rescue.

Marc Dupie was a man with an outspoken gift for finding and making profitable business deals. These have credited his accounts in the biggest banks in America and Europe with millions of dollars and foreign currencies. Marc Dupie's name and reputation were also connected to a travel agency Odyssey Cruise Line. Its headquarters and branch office were on the forty-eighth floor of the Rockefeller Center in Manhattan. He also owned three cruisers: *Aurora*—a tourist ship for river voyages, Oasis for a cruise lines in the United States and between the States and Canada, and an ocean cruiser *Odyssey*. Marc Dupie's plans for the near future were to expand his transatlantic flotilla with yet another cruiser—*Odyssey 2*.

It appeared *A Way of Life* couldn't go out of business even if it wanted to. However, there were two things that could have brought down the popular magazine. The first was if the readers' taste changed, and the other reckless budget spending regardless of the financial plan. Even if struck by a financial crisis, Susan wouldn't ask her father for help. Once she paid him back, the magazine was hers.

Marc Dupie helped the birth of the magazine with his money, even lent it part of his premises in the Rockefeller Center. But the around-the-clock work—hers and that of several enthusiasts and friends along with help from a few faithful sponsors—Susan got on her own feet. She bought the premises in the Rockefeller Center from her father and returned the money she had borrowed. She became self-supporting, but the price of independence was great: She suffered through many sleepless nights, ruined health, and thin nerves. No price could entice her to sell off her independent ownership of the magazine. She fought for it and everything she gained with it like a lioness, watching out for every penny.

That evening she had lost her purse with all the documents, VISA, MasterCard, American Express and Diner's Club cards, and about sixty dollars in cash. The purse got left behind due to a commotion at the end of supper at Sebastian's and was found lying on the table Ethan served. He handed it to Jeffrey Collins, who called Susan Dupie right away. Susan breathed a sigh of relief and thanked him for calling her, saying she would come tomorrow to collect it. At Jeffrey's insisting she allowed one of his men to deliver the purse to her apartment the same evening. That's how Ethan found himself in a taxi on the way to Sutton Place.

Susan Dupie's apartment was on the next-to-last-top floor and had a beautiful view of Queensboro Bridge and Roosevelt Island. On the other side of West Channel, the Goldwater Memorial Hospital and City Hospital were visible.

After the quick ride in the elevator, Ethan stroked his hair, pushed his glasses up on the bridge of his nose with his index finger, adjusting them, and knocked on the door of Susan Dupie's apartment.

A "Coming" responded from the other side, and a woman of about thirty-five appeared at the door. Susan, an attractive brunette with deep and dark eyes, was not the woman who opened the door to Ethan. She had thick, blond hair cascading down to her shoulders. Her eyes shone behind her thin, gold-rimmed glasses and her smile had the same warmth and spontaneity as that of Susan Dupie on her driver's license photograph.

"Good evening," Ethan introduced himself. "I'm coming from Sebastian's. Mr. Collins sent me. Miss Dupie left her purse at our restaurant."

"Ah, yes, that's right. Susan told me you were coming. She apologizes for not receiving you, but she's relaxing in the tub. Not feeling well, too much pressure during the last days."

"I hope it's nothing serious?" Ethan said politely.

"Oh no, nothing of the kind. It's usual for Susan. The headache from working too hard. I keep telling her she works too much and she should take better care of herself, but she won't listen. Often, she ends her day with a headache. She's rather headstrong, you know. She thinks the pills are a remedy for everything. That's her way of getting her problems solved, her headache included. But I don't know why I'm bothering you with all that? You came for another reason."

"No problem, you're not bothering me at all. I hope Miss Dupie will be better soon."

"She will. As soon as she gets rest. I'm sure of that."

"I see," Ethan said, handing over Susan's purse. "Here it is. Please be so kind and give Miss Dupie Mr. Collins's regards and wish her a good night for me."

"I'm afraid this night won't be over for the two of us yet because we still have to look over some papers tonight, but I will gladly convey your regards. I mean yours and Jeffrey's."

"Thank you."

"What did you say your name was?"

"Ethan. Ethan McCoy."

"I'm pleased to meet you, Mr. McCoy. I'm Jessica, Susan's secretary," she offered her hand with a smile that never left her face.

"The pleasure was all mine. I wish you a good night." Ethan said, shaking hands.

"Good night, Mr. McCoy. And thanks again."

14

Ethan was surprised when he saw Susan Dupie and Jessica Bauer in Sebastian's the next day. Jeffrey Collins greeted them with a hearty welcome, which clearly demonstrated that Susan and Jessica were something more than mere customers.

"Hello, Sue, hello, Jess. Honored to see you again in my modest, culinary kingdom. I hope you're not here for a complaint. Should this be the case, I'm not sure my disposition will remain as good as it is thus far."

Susan and Jessica laughed.

"Supper was excellent, Jeffrey," Susan said cheerfully.

"As always," Jessica added, making Jeffrey Collins's spirit rise even higher.

"My dear ladies, what can I do for you then?"

Ethan didn't hear their answer because he went to the kitchen to get an order.

When he returned, Susan and Jessica were still talking to Jeffrey, and all three of them now looked in Ethan's direction.

Ethan hurried to the table occupied by an elderly married couple just as they were leaving. He thanked them for their visit, held the door for them and wished them a good day. The gentleman gave him a polite nod and the lady smiled.

Then he returned to their table and cleared it.

"Good morning, Mr. McCoy. I'm Susan Dupie."

Startled, he knocked a glass against a plate, which produced a resonant sound. Having his back to them, he hadn't seen Susan and Jessica approach.

"I came to thank you personally for finding my purse and bringing it to my home. I want to apologize for not waiting for you."

"That's all right. No problem," Ethan felt more anxiety than he wanted. "Most importantly, you got your belongings back."

"You're very kind. I knew Jeff employs only the best people, but he still surprises me. It's difficult to find honest and unselfish people these days. That's not what New Yorkers are known for. Do you agree?"

"Well, to be honest, I'm not sure. I'm not from New York, and I couldn't say—"

"Indeed not? That explains a lot. How about you tell us during lunch what brought you to New York and where you come from? What do you say about that?"

"You wish to order something?" Bewildered by the speed with which the situation developed and the sensuality and warmth of her voice, Ethan didn't understand the question. He had to admit though, she had captured his attention. And not only his attention. Inside, he sang to the melody of the voice that enriched these moments.

"Mr. McCoy." Jessica turned to him, jostling him away from his thoughts. "We would like you to join us for lunch."

"That's right. You should take it as a small expression of my gratitude." A smile spread over Susan's face.

Flattered by the invitation, Ethan felt his cheeks on fire.

"I'm afraid that won't be possible."

"You won't turn us down, will you?" Jessica's face fell.

"No, no, certainly not. But, I'm working, it's my shift and I'm a waiter here." His self-assurance vanished in a split second as if a cloud came over the sun, covering it.

"Not just *any* waiter, but one of the best, I'm told." Beautiful and merciless, that voice tore down what remained of his resistance. "So, will you join us?" Susan persisted, giving a hidden sign to Jeffrey.

"I would be glad to, but—" Ethan reached for a handkerchief to wipe the sweat from his forehead and buy a few seconds to regain control of the situation, but failed.

"Are we having a problem, young man?" The owner of the restaurant appeared at the table.

Ethan became earnest as if he wasn't that already.

"No, sir, we have none. These two young ladies have expressed their wish to have lunch."

"So, what are you waiting for? Do you need a written order? Why haven't you offered them to sit down?"

"Yes, sir. Right away. . . ."

Susan put an end to Ethan's torture.

"Jeffrey, we've asked Mr. McCoy to join us for lunch, but he seems to be shrinking from the idea."

"Well," Jeffrey rubbed his chin, playing his role. "The truth is we don't approve of employees dining with our guests, especially when on duty. It's against the house rule."

"Can't you make a small exception in this case? Just a little one?" Susan enjoyed her role nonetheless. "I don't need to tell you how much that would increase the ratings of your restaurant in one of the future issues of our magazine."

Jeffrey Collins thought it over before making his mind up.

"Let it be so. But only because it's you. I wouldn't do that for anybody else not for the life of me."

"That's what friends are for." She flashed a wide smile and sat at the table before Ethan could hold out the chair for her.

But he was faster than Jessica and, after some hesitation, he sat on a chair too. He offered a clumsy smile to other guests who watched the whole show with interest, giving him their approval with the nods of their heads and friendly smiles.

He thought the earth would swallow him.

"Isn't it better this way, Mr. McCoy?" Susan addressed him.

"Or Ethan, if I may call you that?"

"Yes, of course."

"And you will call me Susan."

"Okay, Susan."

"Excellent. Now that we've finished getting to know each other, we could order something. What will you have, Ethan?"

For the second time in the last ten minutes, drops of sweat formed on Ethan's forehead when his boss removed the notepad from his pocket to take his order and personally served his employee lunch. Ethan was sure this was his last day at Sebastian's. He knew nothing of the agreement Susan and Jessica had made with his boss.

"How did you like lunch, Ethan?" Susan asked, after finishing the pancakes filled with walnut cream.

"Delicious." He couldn't get accustomed to his new role.

"Sebastian's is one of the best restaurants in Midtown Manhattan. You didn't make a mistake by choosing it."

I didn't make a mistake by choosing it? Good Lord, what would happen if she found out how I came to get this job? Ethan thought to himself.

"The person who recommended it to me spoke nothing but the very best of it," he responded.

"Is that so? What's her name? Perhaps I know her. I move in a wide circle of people and I think I know almost anyone of some significance in New York."

A small bite of the blueberry pie stuck in Ethan's throat. He took a sip of mineral water to push it down.

"I don't think so. That person is my older brother. William Patrick. I don't believe you've heard of him."

"No, I don't think I have. What's your brother's business?"

"He's a sailor," Ethan said, with a little restraint, then hurried to explain. "But I can assure you of one thing, he's definitely crazy about boats. Sailing is his life. He's such a hopeless dreamer. While we're having this conversation, he's probably somewhere out in big waters, sailing on the merchant, *The Nightingale*. I don't know whether that name means anything to you."

"I might surprise you, but I do know of *The Nightingale*. My father's obsession is also ships, so I understand your brother's feelings. I find nothing wrong in being a dreamer. Speaking of someone crazy about ships, what would you say if I told you my father owned three cruisers? If your brother ever decides to switch over from merchant to passenger liners, you just give me a call and I'll talk to him. We'll arrange something."

"Okay," Ethan wasn't surprised by anything anymore. "But you'll have to talk with him about that. I can't speak for him."

"No problem. You send him to me when his ship docks in New York and I'll take care of the rest. Is it a deal?"

"It's a deal."

"Tell us, Ethan, you mentioned before you are not from New York," Jessica joined in. "May I ask where you come from?"

"Yes, that's right. You still owe us that explanation," Susan said. "Where do such nice people come from?"

"I don't believe you've ever heard of Greenfield?"

"Is that in the States?" Jessica cracked a joke and all of them laughed.

"It's a small town in the southwest portion of Nebraska, not far from Scottsbluff. The fields of wheat, barley and corn surround it, together with lots of pastures, the river, and a forest. Rocky Mountains rise in the west."

"I'm afraid, Ethan, geography isn't my strongest side," Susan said. "But I do know where the Rocky Mountains are."

"It sounds perfect," Jessica said in a dreamer's voice. "Don't you think so, Sue?"

"Absolutely. Tell us a bit about Greenfield, Ethan. If we're not bothering you."

"Not in the least." Ethan shook his head. "I'm pleased to have the honor of talking with you."

Jessica gave a mysterious look at her five-year-younger boss and girlfriend who absorbed every word Ethan uttered. And Ethan, carried away as he talked, didn't realize their lunch had already stretched into the third hour.

Like Odyssey, spellbound by the subdued singing of the nymphs, he sailed toward the open seas farther and farther from the land and the lighthouse whose light disappeared in the tide of new and undiscovered worlds.

That lunch took place on Thursday, and the next Tuesday, shortly after eight o'clock in the morning, the telephone rang in the Cranberry Street apartment. Ethan was still sleeping, and the telephone rang for some time before he picked up.

"Good morning. This is Susan Dupie. I'd like to speak to Ethan, Mr. McCoy, if I have the right number."

Ethan was wide-awake in a flash.

"Good morning, Susan. It's Ethan."

"Hello, I didn't recognize your voice right away. Did I wake you up? I apologize."

"No need to apologize. I must get up anyway. But, how come you've called? I mean, I didn't expect your call."

"Forgive me if I did something I shouldn't have done. I talked to Jeffrey, and he gave me your number. I hope you're not angry with me."

"Not at all." On the contrary, he added to himself.

"I'm calling in connection to our conversation in the restaurant. After we parted, Jess and I talked a lot about what you told us."

"Yes?" Ethan asked in expectation.

"Do you know, Ethan, what I do for a living?"

"I heard of your magazine, but I must admit I never had a copy in my hands. I will correct that today when I go out in the city."

"Well, every year we select a new theme for the main topic in each issue of our magazine."

"I'm familiar with that."

"Last year we wrote about food. Healthy food, vegetarian food, food for pregnant women, to name just a few. The year before that we focused on education and professions most attractive to young people. This year it's tourism. Where to spend a vacation, to be exact. It's right here where we need your help. That is, if you're interested and have some spare time."

"I'm listening. I would be glad to be at your disposal, if I can help in any way," he said, though he didn't have the slightest idea how he might help out with tourism.

"Excellent. As I said, our conversation has left a deep impression on Jessica and me. We have agreed that it would be very interesting to make a story of your birthplace and, if it happens to meet our expectations, to put it in one of our next issues."

"Greenfield?"

"Yes."

"But Greenfield is not a tourist town."

"So much the better."

"Excuse me, but I'm afraid you lost me."

"Ethan, average American citizens are inundated with information about well-known and expensive vacation resorts that, when the weight of their pocketbook is calculated, the scale tips the wrong way deflating their enthusiasm. They'd like to have something nice and affordable for themselves and/or their families, different, but not commonplace. Unfortunately, their budget won't allow that. Thus, it becomes an abyss between their desire and the possibility of achieving it, which leads to frustration.

"Tourist agencies have almost nothing new to offer. On the other hand, at least eighty-nine percent of Americans are as familiar with Greenfield as they are familiar with the surface of the Moon. Don't take offense, but it's true. It's here where Jessica and I see its potential. The rural tourism in the middle of the States, with a taste of the Wild West, exotic and adventurous. The union of man and nature at a favorable price. What do you think?"

"Looking at it that way, I think it could hit the jackpot since not many people have heard of Greenfield. Especially east of the Mississippi. But that could also be risky for the same reason. I'm just not sure if it's worth chancing it."

"Life is a risk. When we get out to the street in the morning, we don't know what will happen to us. Some maniac could attack us, a drug addict could rob us for ten dollars in our pocket, or we could get hurt or killed in a street fight by a gang of adolescent delinquents. You leave the risk to us. It comes with our business. Everything new represents a risk. The success and sale of a product depends primarily upon the way it's presented to the consumers. The advertising. We, as far as Greenfield's concerned, have nothing to lose. If Greenfield doesn't meet our expectations, which I doubt, there won't be a story and nobody gets hurt. It's as simple as that. A pleasant memory and several photographs of a trip in an area we wouldn't have known about otherwise."

"I see you've already made up your mind. I only hope printing the Greenfield story doesn't cost unnecessary expenses for your magazine."

"Don't worry about that. Now, Jeffrey told me you took several days off. You are about to travel home on Friday, right?"

"Yes. I took some time off to see how the mill is doing."

"Would you mind some company on your trip? Our photographer Scott and I would like to join you. We should go as soon as possible to check the feasibility of this project and get it rolling if it's what I anticipate."

"That would be great." He made a mental note to thank Jeffrey with a bunch of celery when he returned to work.

"Splendid. Tell me, have you bought the ticket yet?"

"No, I haven't. I planned on doing that the day before leaving. Just in case something pops up."

"Let's keep it that way. We'll take care of that, the rent-a-car included. It's on the house."

"No, Susan. That's out of the question."

"You may consider it as your fee for helping us out. We'll need a guide when we arrive in Greenfield, and guides cost money."

Disarmed, Ethan said, "Okay, I surrender. I'm helpless against such a strong case. I just have to warn you that this guide may finish his part of the job very fast."

"That's what you think. If you make the effort to be as useful and persuasive as on Thursday, you'll do an excellent job, and everybody will be happy."

15

As Ethan suspected, his arrival in Greenfield was a mere formality. Peter performed his duties without fault, and it seemed as if the mill operated at the highest productivity ever. Even better than when Ethan managed it. Finishing his brief inspection, he was convinced his stay would now be a relaxing, short vacation rather than a business trip. Ethan said hello to a few acquaintances, but most of the time he spent with Susan and Scott.

To Ethan's joy, Susan not only was delighted with Greenfield, but sincerely admired it. She called it, "a joker up the sleeve." There was no question of whether or not to publish the Greenfield story. The only question remaining unanswered was how the readers would accept it.

"I knew I could trust you, Ethan. I never doubted your word."

"I'm glad you like it here."

"Like it? This is the place I'd like to spend my vacation more than anywhere else. If only I had time for it. This is a real paradise. An oasis amidst the desert. One can devote time only for oneself here and find inner peace and happiness. That's what we have all lost, thanks to the pressure of work and hectic, everyday life. We have even forgotten the real meaning of that."

They walked along the January River toward the bridge.

Scott focused on the bridge and shot a few more pictures, adding to the hundred and forty images he'd already taken.

"Greenfield seems atypical for this part of the state. It possesses all the hallmarks of the nearby places and towns, yet is so unique. It's much greener."

"That's where its name comes from, green field. However, a good part of this green has been planted by human hand. The first pioneers afforested a lot of it, thus creating a real paradise."

"And all that," Susan made a wide arc with her hand, "proves they succeeded."

"Yes, they did indeed."

"Tell me, Ethan, where does the name January River come from? Any special meaning in it?"

She stared at him with curious eyes as they stopped at the bridge and leaned against the railing. Ethan could not look into the depths of the water. He didn't want to admit to himself that he was still afraid of the ghosts that might surface from below. Instead he shifted his gaze toward Scott lying in the grass and the field flowers that grew under the bridge. Ethan turned his face to the warm, gentle rays of the slowly-setting sun.

"As far as I know, the river was named about a hundred and fifty or two hundred years ago," he continued, as if the ghosts no longer remained in the far currents of the past, silent and undisturbed. "The story passed down over the years says the tribes that lived here called it the Snowy River, and the white pioneers who came later changed its name. The river appeared after an earthquake. The entire Rocky Mountain range shook when it hit. Fortunately, the earthquake caused no damage to this beautiful nature, but something changed the face of this landscape. A river gushed out from the chest of the Rockies."

"The January River," Susan added. "Why did they change the name later into the January River? You're not telling me the quake struck in January, are you?"

Ethan looked into her black eyes with a mild smile. He kept

his gaze locked with them for a fraction longer than it was necessary. Susan felt that. She also felt the warmth of his eyes, in which the beauty of Greenfield, mirroring itself in the evening twilight, found its own reflection. Ethan felt the incredible strength in Susan's eyes, as deep as an abyss. The strength they radiated kept him riveted, not allowing him to wrestle away from them. He wanted to break free, but also wished to give himself over to that power. As though the invisible forces of the universe caught him, and he was at their mercy. Good-natured forces, though, with a positive driving strength. The energy of life from Susan Dupie.

"The earthquake hit one winter, during a snowstorm. That's why the natives called it the Snowy River, while the settlers concluded according to their stories it happened within the first month of the year. In the spirit of the Americanization of this continent, they changed its name to the January River."

"Unbelievable. So simple and yet so romantic. I think I'm falling in love with this place."

"I'm not surprised. That happens to everyone who lands here. The price they pay for coming to Greenfield. They leave a different person."

A flock of wild geese flew above them. Ethan and Susan watched them disappear in the distance. They smiled at each other. Not the usual, ordinary smile. Nor one exchanged between two strangers.

"Fantastic," she whispered. "If we don't leave Greenfield soon, I'm afraid I might stay forever."

"You wouldn't be the only one."

The moment of silence, when neither uttered a word, passed quickly.

"Ethan, if I may openly ask you, what tempted you to leave? It's not clear to me how one can leave this paradise and replace it with a beehive like New York City."

"Perhaps I longed for honey." There was a trace of melancholy in his smile.

"I'm serious. One comes to wish for a little change

sometimes, but you've stayed in New York . . . for how long?"

"About six years."

"Six years. A long time. You must have a reason?"

"Save from needing a change of scenery, I do have a reason why I did that. Life sometimes goes astray, into unusual streams, and then you must swim upstream if you don't want to be dragged down the stream and fall over the waterfall. Do you understand what I'm trying to say?" His eyes darted to the dark waters that silently greeted him from below.

"I understand. We all have floods we have to fight. Some of them turn out to be both very strong and very cold. How did your mum and dad take it when you told them you were leaving? Surely it wasn't all the same to them."

"Hard for them as it was for me. But they had no choice, just as I didn't. I had to think of myself. I'm not selfish, but it was a question of my life."

"You have very nice parents. I wish I had a relationship with my father like that. I'd like to know I mean something to him, more than the money he hoards day after day. He has changed a lot since my mother's death. He's not the man I knew when I was a little girl." Susan looked down at the river. The black tufts of her hair covered her face. Ethan wished he could touch them.

"Everything changes, Susan. We change too, even though we're not aware of it. Only when we turn back and look at the days when we were children, do we see how much we have changed."

"I often ask myself, why it has to be that way. I wish everything could stop for a while and stay so we could enjoy the moment." She looked at him.

"There's an expression for that. Growing up."

"The unstoppable process dragging us away from our innocence."

"You could say that."

"It's comforting to know there are innocent places like this one still on the earth, with innocent people living there."

"I'd rather say less calculating than more innocent. No one

is completely innocent today, Susan."

"Why didn't you tell me you were writing?" she asked suddenly.

"Mother needn't have mentioned it. That was something personal."

"I'm glad she did. You surprise me, Ethan McCoy. How many secrets do you still have? How much is there to know about you that I will find out?"

"There're things you'd regret finding out. The very reason I started writing. That's when I lost my innocence."

"Because you started to write?"

"Because of the reasons that made me want to. Like the one that stole my childhood from me while I was still a little boy and forced me to grow up. It didn't ask me if I wanted it to happen. Nor if I was ready for that."

"I wish I knew you then. When you were still a child."

"Do you think you could have influenced my growing up and slowed it down?"

"No. But I would know how to help you now."

Deep in thought, Ethan turned his face into the shadows, protecting his true feelings from the outer world. Allowing them to remain *his* true feelings. He had so many. In that moment, even more than he had been aware.

"Maybe I'll tell you some day."

"Will you also show me what you've written then?"

"Maybe."

"Too many maybes for such a beautiful evening."

He smiled. "I'll show you what I wrote. It's not personal, and the theme will be familiar to you, anyway."

Susan looked at him, a question in her eyes.

"You'll see," he said, almost whispering.

The next day the visit to Greenfield came to an end. The story done, and the photos that Scott Berger transformed Greenfield into art glossed from the pages of *A Way of Life*.

Leaving Greenfield, Ethan recalled the turmoil of emotions that swirled inside him on every departure occurred this time as before. But now a new emotion accompanied the old ones.

Ethan McCoy knew he had fallen in love with Susan Dupie.

16

Susan Dupie couldn't take her eyes off the manuscript Ethan gave her two days ago. She was pleasantly surprised already with its opening and, as she approached the end of the book, she sped through it like an addict.

Ethan formatted his stories into conversations with celebrities from the literary world. Psychological stories or interviews—as the author referred to them—that cut deep like the sharpest razor, exposing a collection of motives, rationalizations and incitements of the persons interviewed. What forced them into deliberating certain actions which drove them into specific situations and entanglements.

The interviews were conducted with real persons such as Richard Hickock and Perry Smith while they waited on death row. Gary Mark Gilmore was the first convict in America executed after the abolition of the death penalty in 1967. (*The Executioner's Song* was the book upon which the interview was made.) Other interviews were with fictitious characters like Roy Neary from *Close Encounters of the Third Kind*, Danny Forrester from *Battle Cry*, Jack, Danny and Wendy Torrance from *The Shining*, the trumpeter Prewitt from *From Here to Eternity* and Joey Scavello from *Twilight* (later renamed *The Servants of Twilight*). Over twenty other characters found their home on the pages of Ethan's short psychological vignettes.

Not only did Susan think Ethan's idea was clever, she thought the strength of his writing as powerful as the beat of a drum. Original and fresh, success was guaranteed.

Susan didn't easily get Ethan's approval to show the manuscript to Jessica and other colleagues from the editorial staff. She had to "bribe" the talented author with lunches and dinners over which the two of them discussed his work, or indulge him with the strolls along the green parts of New York City when they talked about personal things rather than business. Although the staff members were delighted with what they read and didn't question Ethan's quality as a writer, they were cautious about the whole publishing idea. That made Susan furious, and she almost stormed out on them.

"This is something better than you ever had in your hands and you're telling me to wait?" Her temperament and the readiness to fight came to the fore just as it had when she fought for the first issue of her magazine. "Have you forgotten that the motto of *A Way of Life* is 'getting the jump on others?' That stuff in front of you is *exceptional.*"

"Susan," Ron Davis, one of the senior editors, turned to her. "We agree with you. We're getting the jump on others and this stuff is exceptional. But that could be too big a jump which could take us out of sync."

"What's he talking about?" she turned to Jessica for help.

Her secretary stirred uneasily in her armchair.

"Susan, the complete editorial staff is of the opinion it would be better to wait until 'The Summer in Greenfield' is not such a fresh discovery. If we publish the series of these interviews now. . . ." She shrugged, not finishing her sentence.

Susan was petrified. "You mean—?"

Rarely had she felt put out like she did now, like a hunted she-wolf running from the hunters hungry for fun and killing. Confused, a little insecure and tied to a carrousel of the most varied emotions, she sat in the dock before her colleagues, associates and friends, and had nothing to say in her defense. Because they were right.

In her mind and heart, Susan still did not leave Greenfield. An invisible hand held her captive in a music box of impressions, and she did not want to get out. She sat tiny in it, savoring the still fresh memories of affectionate and warm people she met there, the streets and farms she saw, intoxicated with the smell of wildflowers from the pastures through which she walked with Ethan in the evening hours. Certain someone would open the lid of the box and let her out to dance when the music started, she remained silent.

Her gaze met the expectant gazes of Ron, Jessica and other editors, but what she saw in reality was Ethan's look while he stood on the bridge over the river. He absorbed her image with his gentle, sad and intelligent eyes. Susan could not resist him. She felt more passion, love and fire in him than she had ever felt in Darren. Darren came into her life one morning while she ran along the Hudson River. He asked her if he could keep her company. Intrigued with his green eyes, his smile and the body of a playboy moving by her side effortlessly and graciously as a leopard and not losing breath at all, she accepted a date with him for later that afternoon. It only took a few hours for Susan to stumble before the charm of a young and ambitious Wall Street broker, addicted to squash, gym and jogging. Just as quick as it started, their relationship ended. Both were young, ambitious, and soon they realized that despite the strong, mutual physical attraction their roads were not going in the same direction. Susan remained dedicated to her magazine and left Darren to run without her.

Now, she felt something like that happening again to her. Unlike with Darren, she did not meet Ethan while running because for a long time afterward Susan did not jog in the morning. But what filled her heart, thoughts and inner self to the fullest seemed to be more intense and dangerous than when she was with Darren. Ethan, the complete opposite of Darren, would have been characterized by him as a weakling, if they ever met.

Darren's world had no place for dreamers and romantics. Success, career and prestige were the main and the only things worth devoting oneself to, the only things the society he belonged to acknowledged. Ethan did not care for any of that. Ethan seemed so distant from everything, like a character from a fairy tale or a prince on the white horse girls and women fantasized about, with one difference—he was real, made of flesh and blood. But, nevertheless, that did not stop Susan from dreaming about him. The more time she spent in her thoughts with him the more she became aware of the metamorphosis she was going through, but could not explain to herself yet. That is why she was surprised by what Jessica, Ron and others discreetly tried to tell her and make her understand. She did not realize her feelings were so obvious to others. She didn't because she hadn't even admitted it to herself yet.

She gave a long look to Jessica as her eyes filled with tears. Not tears of shame, but of realization that there are no secrets between girlfriends.

"It's not important what *we* mean." Jessica smiled at her with understanding, knowing what Susan was going through, but remaining unflagging and reasonable. "It's important what *others* will say, our competitors, especially."

"A lot of them can't wait for us to make a wrong move," Davis added, backing up Jessica.

"I don't understand you." Susan tried to hide what was already obvious to everyone, but to no avail. Her hoarse voice was atypically shaking when she confirmed without hesitation, "These interviews will go to press. I've made my decision, and you better make them look their best for the publication."

Nobody opposed her.

What Susan didn't want to admit then she had to accept when Ethan rewrote the material for publication in the magazine and it appeared on the pages of *A Way of Life*. They were accompanied with various inscriptions and comments in the yellow papers and tabloids.

"The Summer in Greenfield" turned into *"A Romance in Greenfield"*

"If you're looking for a real love, come to Greenfield"

"Thinking about your honeymoon? Why not spend it in Greenfield? For useful information, dial the chief editor of A Way of Life*"*

Headlines like these mushroomed all over. Although they raised a lot of dust and noise, there was no real damage.

The articles that appeared in serious papers and weeklies gave expert reviews of the young author's potential and hushed up the mean gossips.

The letters of support from the readers of *A Way of Life* who wished to learn more about the young author behind the name of Ethan McCoy skyrocketed. Ethan McCoy became more famous from one issue of the magazine to the next, shamelessly rocking the literary world of New York City.

After the interviews with fiction and nonfiction characters came the interviews with movie characters. Because a lot more Americans watch TV and go to the movies, this shrewd idea of Susan Dupie's proved to be a turn that launched Ethan McCoy's career into an even greater orbit.

The commotion orchestrated by the yellow press thus helped Ethan to venture into a place he wanted to go, but couldn't quite get up the courage.

He proposed to Susan Dupie, and she accepted.

Without pomp or noise, and with no one knowing except the best woman and best man—Jessica Bauer and Jeffrey Collins—Susan Dupie became Susan McCoy. They sent telegrams announcing their union to William Patrick and Ethan's parents, and when Marc Dupie heard about their marriage, he hit the ceiling, threatening to annul it. Though he had the power and the means, all his threats turned out to be powerless and futile.

The love between two young people was far more powerful than the hatred Marc Dupie harbored toward his lawful, but never acknowledged son-in-law.

Susan then parted from her father. And when they met

again years later, it was too late to change anything.

17

The wind rose, shaking the windows. Ethan thought he better close them before the glass shattered. The aroma of the roast hadn't quite dispelled into the air, yet the terrible thunder accompanied by lightning spread all over the Brooklyn sky. Ethan rushed to close the windows. The air, full of electricity, smelled of ozone and the sea. The torrential rain poured down, blurring his view outside.

Ethan worried about Susan. Where was she now, had she scrambled for cover? She hadn't looked good lately. He worried if she got drenched, she might catch pneumonia.

The storm raging outside the safeness of Will's apartment reminded him of the winter in eighty-six. More than a year ago now. It snowed that day, whipped around by a blizzard. The snowstorm came up so suddenly they had to hurry from the ice-skating rink at the Lower Plaza of the Rockefeller Center. Ethan was none too sorry about that because he had badly battered his posterior and his knees due to many falls. Susan had a jolly good time watching him lose his balance and fall. He was hot under the collar because of his clumsiness. She tried to teach him to skate, and just when he got some self-confidence—he fell again. Four boys and a girl forming a caterpillar by holding one another by their waist dashed past him, causing yet another fall. He shot daggers at the joyful youths. He gazed at the girl with red hair conspicuously projecting from under her knitted green cap and a green shawl. Then he glanced at the last boy in the line and his look stayed fixed on him.

At first, he didn't know what made him stare at the plainly clothed boy. The only thing about him that caught Ethan's attention were his unusually long tufts of blond hair tossing about in the wind. The boy was an excellent skater. When a gust of wind blew the hair away from his face, the divine beauty of a seraph with sky-blue eyes flashed before spellbound Ethan.

The boy looked at him. His eyes met Ethan's just for a second, but that was enough.

A grimace of accusation—an expression of revenge and the unspoken damnation—replaced the perfect smile on the boy's healthy red cheeks.

Ethan's subconscious exploded.

"Et, why didn't you *help* me? I thought we were *friends*?"

Through the sharp pain, Ethan saw a hazy vision before his eyes, and he felt as if he fainted. He didn't know how long this spiritual experience lasted. When he pulled himself together, Susan stood over him, a worried look in her eyes. She was saying something to him.

He looked at her with a question in his eyes.

"Darling, are you okay? Is everything all right?"

He murmured something and looked about, searching the ice rink. In vain. He knew he wouldn't find what he was looking for. That was just an apparition. A ghost as real as the pain in his leg.

The boy with the long tufts dashed past him again, this time alone and skating backwards. He offered him a shining smile as a token of apology. Ethan responded by nodding his head, himself trying to smile. The expression on Susan's face reflected his futile attempt of a smile.

He grinned, and the lines of her face softened.

"I'm all right, thank you. It's just my knee aching like hell."

"Do you want us to sit for a while? Are you sure you didn't break something? You looked like . . . as if you've seen a ghost."

"Let's go," he dropped the subject before she could continue. "I'm fine."

But Ethan wasn't fine. He knew it. His self-assurance depleted, he had enough of ice-skating.

By the time it stopped snowing, Ethan had fallen several times in a row and was therefore delighted by the change of the weather. He could retire from the skating rink gracefully, without arousing concern in Susan's querying eyes.

They went for lunch at the Rainbow Room, a restaurant on the sixty-fifth floor of the RCA building. With the Manhattan skyscrapers wrapped in snow, their silhouettes created a magnificent view for the visitors. Ethan's mood improved. He even laughed several times, too loudly though, attracting the attention from the nearby tables. But he was to be forgiven for that. His laughter radiated cheerfulness, determination and the superhuman will not to let anybody or anything spoil his high spirits. That was a special day for Ethan and Susan, a day to celebrate, and they intended to spend it that way. Celebrating.

The day before they just got the first copy of Ethan's book, simply called *The Interview*. A collection of some twenty of Ethan's conversations with the characters from the world of books and movies. They both had waited eagerly for that moment, seeing, feeling the fruit of their hard work. Ethan McCoy—the author, and Susan McCoy—his agent.

They wanted to celebrate the publication of Ethan's first book appropriately, fitting the occasion. The first time comes only once, when one's first book is published. Like a firstborn child with an indescribable feeling of joy and excitement. No matter how successful the following books turn out to be, that feeling cannot be duplicated.

After lunch, they returned to Will's apartment in which Susan and Ethan now lived. Susan had rented her apartment in Sutton Place and moved in with Ethan. They spent the rest of the day and the evening there. Susan made a couple of phone calls and then cuddled beside Ethan lying on the thick, bushy carpet in front of the fireplace. A cozy place to be, in the arms of her beloved husband, while outside the snowstorm raged.

Ethan embraced her, and she returned his kiss. The wind moaned through the deserted streets while they made love. Forgetting about everything that happened or went on without them, unaware of anyone being born or dying somewhere close or far away, they yielded to their mutual lust.

The doorbell rang, startling them from a pleasant slumber.

Ethan jumped to his feet and got dressed.

"Are you expecting anyone?" he asked, sliding into his pants, while she grabbed her clothes and rushed toward the bathroom.

"No. Do you?" she shouted over her shoulder through the door left ajar.

"I have no idea who could that be at this hour and in this weather."

"It's surely Mrs. Bates," her voice muffled, as she pulled the sweater over her head. "Please, open the door for her. I'll be with you in a minute."

The person standing at the doorway turned out to be a delivery boy, not Mrs. Bates.

Ethan looked at him, surprised. "For me? What could be so urgent that it couldn't wait until the weather calms down?"

"I don't know, sir," a frozen, black boy, in his early twenties, said. He pulled down the knitted cap all the way to his eyes while the collar of his jacket was tightly zipped around his neck. "I only know it's urgent and had to be delivered today."

Ethan signed and gave him a fat tip.

"Thank you very much, sir!" the boy exclaimed, warmed up by Ethan's gesture.

"You deserve it in this weather. Get yourself something hot."

The delivery boy thanked him again and disappeared into the blinding snow.

Ethan had trouble holding the parcel. Something moved

inside banging its sides and making a strange noise. Ethan wondered what it could be.

"Who was it?" Susan peeped out of the bathroom. She watched her husband wrestling with the package as he carried it to the room. She switched off the bathroom light and joined him.

"The delivery boy. Somebody wanted to pull a joke in this weather. I don't know what could be so urgent that it couldn't wait until the blizzard stopped."

"Why don't you open it and look at what's inside?"

"That's exactly what I'm going to do. But snow is all over it and I don't want to get the carpet wet."

"Wait. I'll grab a towel."

"I hope the snow didn't get through these holes." Ethan wiped the package. "It would be just great if it destroyed the contents."

"I don't think so. They wrapped it up well."

"Hope you're right."

He removed the decorative ribbon on the paper and, holding the box, shook it a little.

"Don't!" Susan gasped concerned. "What if it's something fragile? Be gentle."

"No sign of glass inside."

"That's no reason to handle it so roughly."

Ethan looked at her in a puzzled way. "Could you, please, fetch a knife for me?"

"Just be careful." She leaned over him while he cut the cardboard.

A sound came from the box. "What on earth—?" With a sudden movement, he pulled the rest of the wrapping paper away.

"Easy!"

"*I beg your pardon!?*" He stared in the package. "Is this some kind of joke?"

He reached inside and took out a puppy, which, frightened and frozen, shook and shivered all over.

"There's also a note inside," Susan pointed out to him, while Ethan, bewildered, kept the puppy in his arms. "He's adorable, isn't he? Can I hold him for a while?"

Ethan handed her the doggie and reached for the note that lay crumpled at the bottom of the package.

"What breed is it?" Susan asked.

"If I can trust my eyes, I think it's a golden retriever. But how? I'll wring Will's neck if he has a finger in this pie."

He ripped the envelope open and read the note.

To my greatest love of all. Congratulations, and best wishes for your first book.
Susan

Ethan looked at his wife, his mouth agape. She smiled at him rocking the pup in her arms.

"That's yours, I believe. Don't you want him?" She handed the golden retriever pup to him.

"You are mine too," he embraced her.

The puppy wriggled between them, struggling for some air.

"I wanted to give you something special for this occasion," she whispered into his ear.

"But, where did you get the idea?" He raised the puppy to his eye level. The brown eyes watched him with a drowsy look. "How did you know?"

"That this is the right present? I must admit, I did some pondering. Then I remembered your brother telling me you had a dog. That you found him on the riverbank."

The images of the wounded dog lying on the riverbank covered with snow, Ben Zachariah telling him in the crucial moment the most important news of his childhood, Riv smiling at him from the walls of his room in Greenfield. And, finally, a little grave under a maple tree in their backyard. One memory followed by another. Ethan had to fight tears.

"Neither of you talked much about that, and I didn't want to ask questions. I realized it was hard for you to deal with it.

"Ten days ago, Will called here while you were out shopping. We talked a little and then I told him your first book was coming out in print soon. Upon which he almost pierced my eardrum. I asked him for advice on what to buy you as a gift because I was already beside myself from thinking and still hadn't come up with anything. Will didn't hesitate for a second. 'A dog,' he said right away. 'Get him a dog. Ever since he lost his retriever, he's not been the same person. Buy him a dog, Sue, and you will get to know the real Ethan McCoy. You won't regret it. And neither will he.'

"I was afraid of how a dog would affect you, but, the more I thought about it, the more attractive the idea seemed. Then I realized your brother was right. I made lots of phone calls until I picked out a puppy, I liked most."

She scratched the dog behind his ears.

"He's a real cutie," Ethan whispered. "And so frail. I'm afraid I might crush him."

Susan snuggled up against him.

"What's his name?"

"The people I got him from didn't give him one, so I had to name him myself. I hope you'll like it."

"So, what are we going to call him?"

"Tell me first you love me. A lot."

"I love you, Susan McCoy. I love you a lot." He kissed her.

"I love you too, Ethan McCoy." She returned the kiss. "And your doggie, River. January River."

Ethan shivered in her embrace. His eyes gleamed. His throat choked and relaxed by turns.

"A nice name. You picked a nice name."

"The nicest one."

"Thanks, Susan."

"Don't mention it, Mr. McCoy. It's a real pleasure."

The torrential rain calmed down into drizzle. Ethan opened the window again and let the breeze that carried the freshness of the spring enter the room.

With the tinkling of the keys, the door opened, and the draft slammed shut the window he had just opened.

"Hey, you two!" Ethan rebelled. "Do you want to blow me out of the window? Easy now, will you!"

"Sorry, I didn't know you were at the window. Somebody left the windows open on the staircase."

"Hold it, pal! Don't you move. You'll make the whole carpet wet." He rushed toward January River with a towel in his hands. "You had quite a shower." He rubbed the dog's long, wet hair. "You didn't fare any better, either." He turned to his wife who took off her drenched clothes.

"We were only three minutes away from the entrance to the building when it started pouring. Three minutes or an hour wouldn't have mattered. I'd still be soaked. I must take a shower. Supper's ready?"

"Yeah."

"Splendid. I'm starving. The stroll exhausted me. I don't know how much longer I can take him for a walk, if he continues to pull with such strength." She scratched January River under his snout. "Don't you pull me like that anymore, you naughty boy. I'm an old lady who cannot go so fast. I don't have your energy."

"Better hurry with the shower if we're going to fill up your batteries. You look as if he mopped the whole of Brooklyn with you."

Susan stuck out her tongue at him. Then she tossed her wet bra at his head and disappeared into the bathroom.

"What are you thinking about?" she asked him, half an hour later, sipping beer from the cold can. The dog lay beside the table gnawing his bone.

"About everything. While the two of you were out, I recalled when I first met you. I can't believe I acted that stupid."

"I think you were irresistible. Spontaneous, straightforward, and innocent. You made my day. I believe Jessica thought the same."

"Never in my life have I behaved so stupidly. Not before, not after that. I was all mixed-up."

"But you didn't get mixed-up the next time we met. You had everything under control."

"I was on my turf. That's why everything was under control. I felt self-confident because I was familiar with everything."

"We had a great time, didn't we?"

"By all means. After that, I thought about the day when my first book came out in print. Better still, of what happened before it. What you did that cold winter evening, the blizzard didn't stop for hours." He cast a spontaneous look at January River.

"That was a surprise, wasn't it?"

"And how. I don't get how you managed to do that for me. I didn't know whether to get mad at you or to eat you up from joy. I was so confused."

"Had you asked me, I would've told you to eat me up."

"How? Raw? Or to dish you before?"

"The way you like it best." She leaned over the table and kissed him.

"I wonder what surprise you'll have in store for me when *One Step to the Bottom* comes out?"

"You know, I thought about that too. Maybe I'll get another puppy for you. How would you like that?"

"No way. No more puppies." Ethan raised his arms as if protecting himself from an invisible attacker. "That's the last thing I need."

"Why not? I thought of getting a female this time. As we already have January River, we can make a business of raising puppies." She screamed and jumped away from the table when Ethan leaped toward her.

"I'll give you a puppy raising."

"Ethan, don't, the dog's watching us!"

18

The second book by Ethan McCoy was scheduled for publication in the spring of 1988. Unlike *The Interview*, which became an instant bestseller in the States, *One Step to the Bottom* didn't quite mimic its success.

The novella was about the hours-long night exchange between a potential suicide victim who left his telephone number on a live radio broadcast wishing for female companionship and conversation. A woman answered his call. The usual and informal chat turned into a real battle for life that lasted until dawn when a desperate man planned to kill himself. The woman, also feeling lonely that evening and wanting to talk to someone as a friend, had to find and give a good reason to the desperate man to keep living—all within several hours. The conversation took place on Christmas Eve.

Ethan's first solo work *One Step to the Bottom*, pushed its way into the top fifteen bestsellers and also received commendable critiques and reviews. This time he didn't insert himself into the story of the popular bestseller, where he met their heroes and—at a particular, usually crucial moment of the plot—asked them for an interview.

Evidence of his first step indicating that Ethan McCoy

swam into different creative waters, resulting in the loss of a small part of his readers. However, to the pleasure of his most faithful readers who launched his career helping him to become a celebrity, he also continued writing interviews which brought him fame and his own niche.

The publishing of *One Step to the Bottom* wasn't accompanied with all the celebration and rejoicing as *The Interview*. Susan gave Ethan no present to mark the publication of his second book.

The worst part of the whole occasion was the second heart attack Sean McCoy suffered, and to which he succumbed.

A period of heavy depression came over Ethan and Susan. If not for Susan, Ethan wouldn't have known how to get over those hard times by himself.

"I love you, Et, I love you very much," she kept telling him trying to offer consolation, though she herself was shaken with the loss and needed consoling too.

"I love you too, my dear. I love you very much. And I wouldn't know what to do if I lost you. You're everything to me. You've rescued me. And returned my hope when I had stopped expecting anything from life. You chased away the nightmares that haunted me. But they're coming back again, now that my father passed away."

"I don't know what I would do without you, darling, either. The very thought I could lose you someday scares me so much that it physically hurts. That is the nightmare that sneaks around me ever since my mother's death and it doesn't go away. I don't want to lose you, Ethan. I couldn't stand that."

"You won't lose me, Sue, I promise. I'm your husband and I'll be that forever. The future's before us, we love each other, and I wouldn't dream of leaving you."

"And if we would have to part someday . . . ?"

"We won't part."

"We can't be sure."

"Hush."

"My mum and dad thought they would never part. And then she died. Two worlds collapsed with her. My dad's and mine.

My dad had plenty of money, but no amount could buy her life. All his wealth lost its glitter at that moment. His money proved to be useless.

"I was a little girl when it happened, but I remember very well how my father changed after that. He became a different man. Cold, emotionless. He showed no feelings or empathy for the suffering or problems of others. Jealous of anyone who was happy, he couldn't stand seeing a smiling face. I think he died the day of my mom's death."

"I know how you felt. My father's death still hurts so much, and I'm a grown man. I thought I'd go crazy when he died. I couldn't believe it when my mother called. I was mad, furious at him. Angry because he didn't give me a chance to say goodbye and tell him I loved him. Susan, I loved him very much. I wanted to ask him to forgive me if I had ever let him down. But I never got the chance.

"I can hardly remember his funeral even though it happened recently. I know it rained. And that you were with me, squeezing my hand. My mother was crying, which she rarely did. Will held her while I stood helplessly beside them. Everything seemed sort of strange, surreal. As if I was miles away, and then again, the sentiments were right there with me. They traveled invisible routes, sending painful signals to my heart.

"I do remember I had a bad headache. Father Bell read verses from Ecclesiastes about fears in our way and the flourishing almond tree and failed desire because we will mourn a beloved someone who will go to his long home; the loosed silver cord, broken golden bowl or the pitcher at the fountain and the wheel at the cistern, for the dust will return to the earth and the spirit unto God who gave it.

"I clearly heard and understood those verses at the moment of the greatest sorrow, but I wasn't present during the prayer anymore. I was running away from that rain and Greenfield, I was running into the sunshine, but again I remained in Greenfield. I was groping in the dark. Then I saw Der. I saw him standing on the bridge, I heard my voice as I yelled, but he was falling already. He splashed into the water and disappeared. I leaped after him to look for him, but he wasn't there. I swam to the surface to get a breath of air, but his hand clutched my ankle and pulled me back into the depths. Then you pinched me, and I realized I was in the graveyard and that people were already leaving. They walked fast to get away from the rain."

If he could have chosen, Ethan would have pledged everything for the possibility to bury something else instead of his father in the open grave beside him while he watched the earth cover fresh flowers. The phantom, rising from the Greenfield soil, came to life again at night, in his dreams. He wanted to bury the phantom who stole all the good memories of Derrick, leaving in their place scars of suffering, uneasiness, and fear.

The fretting of the soul.

And damnation of the vow of silence.

Ethan knew the ugly vision of his childhood friend wouldn't give him peace until he did something about it. He also knew he wasn't ready for that yet, that he didn't have courage.

So, he agreed to pay the price for it. The price of fear.

Ethan's heart still couldn't find its peace.

"You see, Sue, it is hard when we lose someone we loved. Very hard. We'll all leave one day. Someone sooner, the other one later. But the end comes to all of us whether or not we like it. Those that remain behind, those we leave behind, they continue to live. They move on, no matter how hard it is for them. Nobody asks them if they would rather lie down, fall asleep, and never rise again. Nobody asks them, but they carry on."

"But I couldn't go on if I lost you, Ethan. I couldn't. . . ."

"You won't lose me, don't be afraid. You won't lose me."

He held his beloved wife in his embrace, and she cuddled on his chest.

"It seems some nightmares always remain with us. As if they become part of us." He wiped the tears from her face. "If they disappeared, it would end us. That's why they don't go away. As long as they live with us, we live. When they die, we die."

"Dark secrets of the heart."

"Exactly."

"I love you, Ethan McCoy."

"I love you too, Mrs. Ethan McCoy."

The next few days, both Ethan and Susan applied themselves to their respective work. Susan developed a new magazine theme for the upcoming year, while Ethan plunged into his new novel.

They both got cracking. Occasionally, Ethan stopped writing and watched his thoughtful wife as she scribbled on her papers, unaware that he was watching her. A smile of contentment twittered on his tired face as he watched her from the other end of the room where he sat with his laptop, happy to be in her presence.

Though Ethan McCoy was a happy man, he wouldn't describe his life as a bed of roses. However, he thought his current one came pretty close. As if Susan McCoy compensated for the loss of his loved ones, parting of friendships, and all the tears he shed. Had he been forgiven? His sins of his childhood erased and undone the lives he destroyed?

Ethan McCoy didn't dare accept that luck smiled upon him. He knew how fickle it could be. But then again, with the close proximity of his wife inside the warmth of their home, which she created, he could not deny his happiness. In fact, he might just be one of the happiest men alive.

He wondered whether she was just as happy. Did he make her feel satisfied and fulfilled? Alive? To Ethan, it seemed the fire of life in her pupils had started to flicker. Those magnificent pupils, and magic eyes. As if something was going on Susan didn't want to tell him about.

Was it possible there were things she kept to herself? Unshared secrets between them? No, Susan wouldn't do that. She would tell him if something was wrong. Always open and candid, as only she knew how to be.

Those were her virtues: openness, candor.

Ethan believed that open and candid people had lots of enemies. Either because they created them or they were *different*. It took courage to be like that and if anyone had it, it was Susan. Ethan admired her skill for avoiding making enemies while keeping her friends at the same time. Only exceptional people manage to do so.

Unique, she manifested more determination than most people. And yet people loved and welcomed her into their company. Convinced nobody disliked Susan, Ethan believed she attracted people because of her virtues and personality traits.

Susan was full of virtues.

And Ethan adored every part of her.

He forced himself to change his train of thought from Susan to his writing. Though not easy, he had to. *The World Beyond*, inspired by Elvis Presley's "In the Ghetto," was at that crucial stage of developing a story and, if he didn't knuckle down now, everything would dissolve and fall into pieces. If he interrupted his writing at this stage, depression would be back and then nobody could tell for certain when he would write again.

Everything would roll the same away.

The wheel of misfortune would start to spin again. If he somehow didn't prevent it.

With a sigh, he continued writing.

The World Beyond saw the light of day in the fall of 1992, after many years of pausing. It was the first of Ethan's books to reach number one and stay there for a full six weeks.

Thus, the name Ethan McCoy joined the names of renowned artists and masters of the pen like Dean Koontz, Stephen King, Anne Rice, Ken Follett, and many others.

While *The World Beyond* drew readers' and critics' attention, Ethan McCoy worked on an outline for his new novel, *Dark Secrets of the Heart*. The last and biggest interview with Ethan McCoy.

However, life turned its back on Ethan once again, thus justifying his doubts and fears. Ethan had to stop writing before he even started.

Susan fell ill. After she tried to remedy the headaches, dizziness, loss of appetite, sweating, and flu with over-the-counter medicines, she finally sought medical treatment. Ethan made an appointment with her doctor and arranged for an examination.

The diagnosis was: *Acute myeloid leukemia.*

Susan refused to accept the diagnosis, convinced that Dr. Raymond Parkins made an error somewhere and somehow. She insisted they repeat the examination. Parkins assured her it was pointless, but gave in to Ethan's request. The second diagnosis confirmed the first.

Acute myeloid leukemia.

Fear crept into Susan and she began to shiver. When she pulled herself together, she started to cry. Ethan's efforts to console her were fruitless. Raymond Parkins gave her a tranquilizer and, while a nurse remained with Susan, Ethan went out with him into the corridor.

"Mister McCoy, your wife's seriously ill. She should remain in the hospital for treatment."

"How ill? What does it mean, acute—?"

"Myeloid leukemia. It's a cancer of the blood and bone marrow. Your wife's bone marrow has made abnormal myeloblasts, a type of white blood cell. Normally in charge of fighting infection, they became unhealthy, malignant. To put it simply, your wife should remain in the hospital and undergo chemotherapy to enable us to destroy the carcinogenic cells in the bone marrow and pave the way for creation of normal ones."

"Excuse me, but I don't believe Susan will accept it. I don't believe she'll agree to stay in the hospital."

"I'm afraid your wife is not in a position to decide. The chemotherapy is necessary, and the need to start is urgent. Even so, we cannot guarantee the leukemia won't return. We know that from experience."

"Then why have chemotherapy, if it cannot help her?"

"It's a step toward a bone marrow transplantation. Don't worry, it's not as horrible as it may sound. Should we find a donor who has a genetic structure corresponding to the one of your wife, the chances of her survival would grow significantly. Almost by hundred percent."

"The chances of her survival?! Are you trying to tell me that Susan could die?" The reality hit Ethan with all its brutality.

"I'm sorry I have to tell you this, but if she doesn't undergo the transplant, she very likely will."

Ethan was on the verge of hysteria. "When can you start the treatment?"

"The chemotherapy, right away. The transplant, as soon as we find the donor."

"Haven't you got one?"

"We haven't, Mr. McCoy. At this moment, we have no one who fits your wife's profile."

"When will you have one? Could I be the donor?"

"We'll do the tests on you as well. But that doesn't mean you'll be a match."

"What are the chances you'll find someone who will be a match in case I'm not."

"They're about the same."

"About the same?"

"Yes."

"And if you don't. . . ."

"You better join us in prayer that we find one, Mr. McCoy. Don't think about that now."

19

Ethan packed up his belongings and brought them to the car, then went back to the apartment once more. He looked all around the room. Different from the one he moved into fourteen years ago, but then after all, in some ways the same one. That old one. When Susan moved in with him, they agreed to redecorate it. The first thing they changed was a built-in fireplace that improved the look of the apartment so much they gave up on other upgrades they originally had in mind. They whitewashed the walls, bought a new carpet, re-furnished the living room, and bought new high-tech music equipment—a present for Will. It was also the bait to mollify him for turning his apartment upside-down without his knowledge.

When Will saw the redecorated apartment, he stopped dead as if petrified. He thought he must have mistaken the floor. But Ethan and Susan laughed at his reaction so heartily that he knew he hadn't. That was his apartment, all right, or wasn't it? When he pulled himself together and looked at the changes they made, he realized his brother and sister-in-law did an excellent job. He congratulated them and thanked them for the music equipment.

And now, Ethan was leaving the apartment in which he spent so many nice, but also sad moments toward the end.

Worst of all was Susan's death. After a year of chemotherapy, expectations, false hopes, shed and unshed tears, and smiles.

Exhausted from the treatment without positive results and tired of waiting for a donor they never found, Susan decided not to take any more chemotherapy and left the hospital. She felt like a laboratory rat and wanted to keep what little dignity she had left until the end. She was fed up with the smell of a hospital, shots, the side effects of the prescribed medications, and Raymond Parkins' false optimism. The only thing she cared about was the time she still had and wanted to spend it with her husband. She took all the toil for his sake only. If not for Ethan, Susan would never have allowed it. She did it because of his love for her.

That was the last thing she could do for him. She'd run out of time to conceive the child he wanted so much. Undergoing the hospital treatment was the last gift to her husband, she had to leave behind. It wasn't the time to be selfish and kill his hope ahead of time.

Yes, Susan knew she was dying. She felt the time for a donor had passed even if they found one. It was already too late. She had no strength to undergo another operation, al-though Raymond Parkins assured her that bone-marrow transplantation wasn't your typical operation. For her, it was another puncture. She vowed never to suffer through any more injections even if it might save her life.

She lay in their bed, weak, exhausted, and pale. Her milky complexion was almost transparent. Her eyes were heavy and red from crying, her arms and legs slender like sticks. She experienced moments when she felt better. When Jessica or Mrs. Bates visited, she enjoyed their company. Mrs. Bates brought lunch for the two of them every day. They sat with her for hours and her spirits rose. But most of all she enjoyed the conversations with her husband, who would retell their adventures in his funny way that always made her laugh.

"Do you remember how you stopped those boys at Bethesda Fountain when we were in Central Park and asked if one of them could lend you his Rollerblades? You set them back on their heels. I'm sure nobody ever asked such a crazy thing before."

"And the most daring one. . . . What was his name?"

"Jamie."

"Yes, Jamie. Then Jamie made a few circles around us skating backward and said—"

"If you can do that, Ma'am, they're yours for a few minutes."

"And I said to him, 'Hand them over, young man, and I'll show you what I know.'"

"He took off his Rollerblades and gave them to you. I couldn't believe it. Do you remember how he shouted after you when you sped off?"

"Ma'am, watch out, don't hurt yourself!"

They both laughed.

"When you disappeared, he looked at me with a worried look and asked if you were coming back. I answered that he had me as insurance, so not to worry. You should've seen his face. I didn't think I was that repulsive."

"You aren't, but he wasn't interested, you're a guy. If I'd been in your place, Jamie would've forgotten about his skates and prayed to God you never returned."

"You're probably right," a smile flickered on his face. "Do you remember when River jumped on a street hydrant the kids had opened to cool themselves down? As he leaped into the gushing spout, they ran off, head over heels."

"And what do you think it looked like when his owner jumped into that spout of water after him? In his dress trousers and wearing a brand-new tie? Can you imagine the image? You, soaked to the skin, wandering the streets until we got home?"

Ethan's laughter was contagious. "As far as I recall, that was quite a sight for women's eyes. Never in my life have so many women turned their heads and looked at me as then."

"I could've plucked their eyes out. But I couldn't blame them. You were so hot."

"Those were crazy times," Ethan said, with nostalgia in his voice. "And that late afternoon when we stood at the window, hugging each other and watching the sunset, when a hawk grabbed a pigeon right in front of our eyes?"

"Poor pigeon. I couldn't watch that."

"And those silly dog walkers. How many dogs the woman held onto the leash and got tangled up and fell? Six, or seven?"

"Perhaps more. Quite a furry bunch, all over her, barking their lungs out."

"And when we played street ball with those kids from our block? Wasn't that something? It was the real thing. You were all sweaty, without a breath, but still smiling. And so gorgeous."

Where did he draw his strength from? Susan kept asking herself. Where did he find the energy to give her morale a boost?

That was her Ethan. Her husband. Her only joy and happiness when she had lost everything. Marc had treated him with such anger and loathing when she left the hospital. Her own father made a scene, pouncing on Ethan as if he were to blame for everything. Ethan almost came to blows with him. Thank goodness, the doctors prevented the ruckus from escalating.

Susan couldn't understand how he could have done such a thing to her. She was dying, and he spat so much hatred toward a man she loved with all her heart. Couldn't he control himself at least then and let her die in peace? Pretending everything was all right, though she knew nothing was right and that her death would only make things even worse. No, that was too much for him. She couldn't ask that of her father.

Marc Dupie had no feelings and no understanding. He became a monster. He destroyed everything around him. And now he wanted to demolish what remained of her life.

She would've hated him had she still the strength. Despised him. The man who was once her father now disgusted her.

At the end of her lifetime, she tried to imagine what her mother's last moments may have been like. What was it like to live with such a man? Had he shown the signs of mental disorder even then, or did he become like that later? She pitied her

mother. She was sorry she was so little and couldn't offer con-
dolences to make her last moments a bit nicer. She felt sorry her
mother didn't have someone like Ethan McCoy beside her.

How much she loved that man. All her life-strength con-
centrated on love for him, and that was the only thing that still
kept her alive. She didn't believe in medicines and their power
anymore. She had a good reason for that. No, she had two good
reasons. They didn't help her mother (she succumbed to a gall
bladder operation), and they didn't help her either. Susan only
believed in something that had the power over death, and that
was love. Love was the meaning of her life and Susan lived for
love and because of love. She would have lived on for thousands
of years on the love itself—she had so much love in her. But her
body didn't have the strength to match. It weakened by the minute. It disobeyed and was failing her. But her love grew, gaining
new strength. It would outlive her, that love of hers. She would
continue to live in Ethan when she wouldn't be there anymore.
Susan would never leave him and would be with him as long as
he lived.

She called Ethan when Mrs. Bates left and asked him to
come to her.

Ethan stretched himself next to her on the bed, embraced
her, and kissed her forehead. "What can I do for you, darling?"
he said, stroking her thin hair.

"Ethan, I would like to ask you something while I still have
the strength. It is very important to me so please don't say no
until you hear everything, I have to say to you."

"I'm listening."

"I had two loves in my life. You are my sincerest and greatest love. But before you there was someone else. My first love
was *A Way of Life*. In my last will, which is with my lawyer, I
leave it to you. I want you to know I don't expect you, nor do I
oblige you to continue where I have stopped. I know how painful for you that would be. Do with it whatever you like. That
won't be my worry anymore. Do whatever you think would be
the best for you. Sell it, sink it, I don't care. But please,

whichever way it turns out, take care of the people who work there. They are my friends, and most of them were like a family. Should they wish to leave, give them the indemnity and take care of them until they find something else. I wouldn't like them to end up on the street. I owe them too much in many ways."

"You can rest assured about that. Everything's going to be all right, I promise. I'll take care of them."

"Thank you. There is one more thing. I must ask you to do something I simply cannot leave to a chance. It concerns you. Take that as my last wish, Ethan, and continue to live. No, no. Don't interrupt me. Let me finish. Okay? Thanks, dear. Please don't die with me and turn into my father. I could never forgive myself for that. I want you to finish what I interrupted you from doing and bring the novel to its end. Do it for yourself as well as for me. Do it for Will and for your friends in Greenfield. Do it for what you loved all your life, and what has become a part of you. And never stop loving. Never stop giving love. Because everything we had doesn't make any sense then. Everything we created becomes lifeless and disappears. Don't let that happen, darling."

"I will not, love," he whispered, in her ear, while the tears rolled down his cheeks. "I will not allow us to disappear."

"Thank you."

Several minutes went by until Susan spoke again. Her voice was subdued and resembled a whisper.

"You know, now that I'm leaving, it might be easier for me to believe . . . in your God. To know there is someone who will take care of you and watch over you when I'm gone."

"You believe in Him, dear. You believe in Him. You believe in love, and He is perfect love."

After a while Susan fell asleep. One hour later she died in her sleep.

In the embrace of her husband.

Shaken by these memories, Ethan blew his nose and wiped his eyes wet from crying. He remembered the words he said to Susan about how we all die, but those who remain go on. No matter how hard for them that may be. It was only now he realized the weight of what he had promised to her then.

He descended to Mrs. Bates' apartment, where January River waited for him, wagging his tail.

"So, you are leaving," Mrs. Bates said.

"I am. I think I took everything. Here's the key. Please, look after the apartment while Will's gone. I left him the message on the table. I would like everything to be in order when he returns."

"You shouldn't worry. Everything will wait for him just as you left it."

"Thank you, Mrs. Bates."

"We shall miss you. Both you and Susan. And you too, little furry ball," she stroked the dog who reached out his paw. "Oh, you would like to say goodbye? You're in such a hurry to leave me, aren't you?"

"Thanks again for everything, Mrs. Bates. You've been a real treasure."

"Nonsense, boy. Love thy neighbor and help him in his trouble—that's the whole wisdom. That's what the Bible teaches us. Besides, I'm being paid to look after the house."

"You're right. That's all the wisdom. But few people keep to that."

He embraced the weak, old lady who kissed both his cheeks.

"I wish you nothing but the best, my dear boy. May God look after you. And drop me a line when you arrive in Montana. I will wait for your card."

"I will, Mrs. Bates. I won't forget you. A part of me will always think of you."

"Go now, before you make me cry. That won't do my old heart any good."

He smiled at her and got in the car without saying another word.

A moment later he left Brooklyn forever.

20

Susan's funeral took place two days after her death. The day was sunny, windy, and a bit fresh. Hundreds of people came to see her off for the last time. The complete staff of *A Way of Life* was there, numerous journalists and reporters from other papers and magazines, as well as two TV crews. Will, who learned of Susan's death in the port in South America, also attended the funeral, arriving at the last moment. After spending the rest of the day with his brother, he returned to the *Odyssey*. During the ceremony, Ethan and Marc Dupie never looked at each other, nor exchanged a single word.

The next day, Marc Dupie called Ethan. He wanted to meet with him and have a word. Ethan responded that they had nothing to talk about when Susan was alive, so he didn't see the point in talking to him now. That infuriated Marc Dupie. He raged over the phone, threatening Ethan and warning him to keep his sticky fingers away from *A Way of Life*. He would rather die than let him get a hold of it as he did with his daughter. Should he not listen and take him seriously, he'd fire his brother and make it impossible for him to get another job on any ship for as long as he lived. Marc Dupie asked himself why he didn't fire him already and thus broke up with the damned McCoys once and for all.

Ethan ignored all the insults and told Marc Dupie that he had no intention of keeping Susan's magazine. As far as he was concerned, he could take it. As for the private transactions, he should turn to Susan's lawyer because his time was too valuable to waste it on such a conversation. Ethan couldn't help himself not to exult when he sensed the bewilderment and insecurity in the voice of Marc Dupie before he hung up on him.

Before renouncing *A Way of Life*, Ethan had a stipulation added to the contract providing that the new owner, Marc Dupie, had to keep all the staff who would wish to continue to work for the new owner. As for those wishing to leave, the new owner had to provide them with an indemnity amount of one-year's pay at the time when the business of the magazine was at its best. Marc Dupie signed the document and *A Way of Life* thus became his.

The majority of the employees expressed a desire to leave. Those were the people closest to Susan, those who worked with her the most. When after a year the magazine bankrupted, the others had to go too.

A Way of Life died a year after its long-term owner.

Ethan McCoy honored the promise to his dead wife.

There weren't many people at Sebastian's. Ethan was surprised how only a few sat at the tables.

"What can I do," Jeffrey Collins lamented. "Ever since you left, the business fell. Everything has changed. Have you maybe changed your mind? Your place here will always be waiting for you."

"Thank you, sir." Ethan still called Jeffrey Collins sir, even after nine years when he stopped working at Sebastian's. "But it's not gonna happen. I'm leaving New York tonight and I dropped in just to say goodbye. And to treat my new agent to lunch before we sign the papers."

"In that case, there's nothing I can add to that. What would your new agent and you like to order?"

"The same we had when we ate here together the first time. If my collaborator doesn't mind, and if you still remember our orders."

"Your collaborator is so hungry she would eat anything," Jessica laughed. "Your order seems just perfect," she added.

"Great. And you, sir? Do you remember what you should bring us?"

"My memory's still serving me well. At least that much," he said, in a tone of voice as if he took offense and marched into the kitchen.

An outburst of laughter followed him.

The lunch went in silence, interrupted from time to time by the tinkling of forks and knives, and occasional memories.

"I cannot believe eleven years have passed," Jessica said.

"Time flies. It'll pass us by in a flash if we're not careful. Fortunately, Jess, you still look the same as that day when Susan and you came here looking for me."

"And you are still as chivalrous as you were ten years ago. Pity I'm not a bit younger."

"If you were younger, you wouldn't be interested in chivalrous gentlemen. You'd run after some of those skaters, instead."

Jessica burst out laughing. "You've got a point here, you know. The idea doesn't seem bad at all."

"Jess, mind what you're saying. Jeffrey's watching you in a somewhat suspicious way."

Jessica turned around and waved to Jeffrey. "Jeffrey and I are old friends. So old that we're not interested in each other."

"I don't know why, but I wish it wasn't so."

Jessica said nothing in return.

"Well, we should get down to business. Riv's waiting for me. He's as impatient to get going as much as I am."

"Okay."

"Have you read the papers I left you?"

Jessica nodded her head and Ethan continued, "Those are

the terms upon which Susan acted as my agent closing the deals for me. I changed nothing. The copies of my old contracts with the publishers are also enclosed. I'm keeping the originals with me. When time comes to extend or end one of my contracts, that is when you show up, looking for a new publisher if there are interested parties. You're taking it from there. But don't make any big decisions before consulting with me first. I don't need money and I don't care about it, but I don't want to be taken advantage of either. Okay?"

"I understand."

"Here are my terms for the book I'm working on. I should finish the manuscript in about four to five months time and then I'll send it to you. Once the publisher accepts it and the proof-reading is done and it is ready for printing, I leave it to you. I don't want to see it ever again. My job's done and from here on, everything's in your hands. Do you think you can take care of that?"

"Ethan, what do you think I've been doing all those years with Susan? Of course, I can handle it. Everything will be done as you wish."

"I have full confidence in you, Jess. I know you won't disappoint me. As you haven't ever disappointed Susan."

Although they both spoke freely about her, the memory of Susan still hurt too much.

"I still miss her, Ethan. I wonder whether I'll ever grow accustomed to life without her in it. She radiated such energy and was always nice to everyone."

"Tell me about it."

"Forgive me, I'm so inconsiderate. You were her husband, not me."

"When you truly love someone, it doesn't matter if you were friends or spouses. It hurts the same. Death's not something natural, Jess. It's a curse. If that weren't so, it wouldn't hurt this much."

"I never thought of it that way, but I think you may be right. Nobody wants to die. We all feel resistance when our time comes. I don't understand people who kill themselves. Don't they know how miserable our lives are even without them? I wish I knew what they feel when they're dying. Do they feel any remorse at all?"

"Some do, some don't. Some have remorse and atone, and to others it's all the same. If you want to get a better insight in their state of mind, I suggest you read *The Interview* by Ethan McCoy."

"You got me there. I have to give you a credit for that."

"But I didn't get your signature yet. Will you make those papers legal so I can go?"

"Sure. Just let me put my glasses on."

"So, that's done. You'll hear from me as soon as I get settled. I don't know yet where the road will take me."

"Except that it's going to be in the Treasure State?"

"Yes, except that."

"Why that far, Ethan? Why Montana?"

"I don't know. I'm not sure. Always wanted to see Montana, ever since I was a little boy. It's beautiful there. Many rivers, plenty of water. Perhaps, I can blame Larry McMurtry for that. Who knows? I'll probably like it."

"I truly want you to like it there. And that you recover from everything. You need to gather your strength if you're planning on repeating the success of *The World Beyond*."

"And wits, Jess. And wits too."

He went to pay the bill, but Jeffrey didn't want to take the money. "It's on the house," he said. "A small goodbye gift from a friend." Ethan thanked him, bid farewell, and then said goodbye to Jessica.

Before he went to collect his belongings and January River, being looked after by Mrs. Bates, Ethan wanted to do one more thing. He slipped into his Rover and drove to the graveyard.

He couldn't leave without saying goodbye to Susan.

21

Sixteen days had passed since Susan's death. To Ethan, they seemed like an eternity. Like a nightmare that dragged on forever. Without a beginning, without an end. He couldn't get into his head how life could be so cruel and so fickle. First, it gave you everything, only to take it away from you the very next day. This had already happened to him a long time ago. He lost everything before when he was left without his friend, dog, childhood, and his father in Greenfield.

When he met Susan, she kind of made up for everything that happened to him. Nothing returned, because what goes away cannot be brought back. Ever. But with Susan, he forgot about the pain, his depression, the loneliness and injustice for quite some time. He opened his eyes and found joy, happiness, love and the beauty in life. He also found peace and tranquility he longed for so much, no matter how fickle and deceptive they were. All those petty joys he rejoiced in as a boy, and had died in Greenfield, were resurrected again with Susan.

Susan made a man out of him. She made him a writer, a husband, a star. She awakened in him all those values and self-respect he tried to bury deep inside himself for years, keeping them prisoners in a world of trepidation, uncertainty, and self-

criticism. Her optimism, her serenity, her *willpower*, and indestructible strength brought them back into the daylight. Most of
all Susan's strength, which flickered only once. But then the
flame died and she was gone. Susan taught him how to live on
with his secrets, how not to be afraid of the memories, but to
remember with joy everything and everyone he loved.

In his twenty-eighth year of life she afforded him indescribable joy. She said yes to becoming Mrs. McCoy and married him.
They spent the honeymoon in Disney World, Cape Kennedy,
and the shores of Florida. From that moment on, his life got
meaningful. He was fulfilled and happy. Successful. Ethan
loved, and Ethan was loved. He had someone close with whom
he could share the nice and the bad moments. His visions and
his nightmares. His thoughts.

He had his wife—Susan McCoy.

Ethan could not comprehend he was alone again. Alone,
with only January River by his side. He didn't want to accept it.
The last lights of New York City—the city that opened its doors
to him and gave him the chance to make a new start—remained
a long way behind as he drove along the Interstate 80. A much
longer and strenuous drive still lay before him. The dark-green
Rover glided through the deep-blue night, and Bruce Spring-
steen sang "The River" on the radio. After him, Roy Orbison
started his "Mystery Girl."

Slowly and unconsciously Ethan increased the speed as his
mixed sentiments got stronger and stronger. He sped toward the
night and the lights of the cars coming from the opposite direction. Without his mysterious guide, without her magic eyes,
without the miracles she performed for him.

Without the girl who wasn't mysterious to Ethan, but was
his wife Susan with deep, dark eyes that held him prisoner, and
whose extinguished light turned Ethan's paradise into hell. Leaving him to burn out completely.

In his memory, in his pain, loss, suffocated passion.

In his love.

Jon Secada's "Just Another Day," one of the hottest

numbers in the past several years, started to play. Ethan hummed along with the melody he remembered so well. The wind tousled his hair through the open window, but it also tousled his thoughts and the images appearing and disappearing in them.

Spilling like the watercolors in the rain.

The sentiments overwhelmed him, and the tears rolled down his cheeks, blurring his sight. The road in front of him spilled into a river of memories.

He stepped on the gas pedal and thinking he didn't want to make it through the day without Susan, sang loudly along with Jon Secada.

Just another day.

22

Ethan arrived to a pleasant and sunny forenoon in Greenfield. The temperature rose by the hour, indicating warmer weather. Ethan didn't stay in the town, but drove straight to the river. He wanted to show his friend, River, the places where he had spent many pleasant moments as a boy. He showed him the spot where he had found his predecessor on a cold and windy January late afternoon. River felt something was going on with his guardian—as if some inner creature, some tiny dwarf played with his feelings—so he tried to attract Ethan's attention with his liveliness and sprightliness. Ethan grabbed him by the scruff, shook his head, and then broke into a run. The golden retriever followed him.

He took a swim in the river and stretched out in the shadow of a small grove where he had relaxed and meditated when he was much younger. And it was precisely there, in that small grove, where he found the remains of the raft that Will broke apart following Derrick's death. The event that changed his life and several others' too.

About three o'clock in the afternoon—after a few hours of reminiscing that seemed as long as years, but passed in a flick of the moment—he felt a huge hunger. The last time he put something in his mouth was four hours ago, and he also had to feed River. He dressed, started the engine, and drove away on a trailing throttle. He drove slowly along the bank of the river and sped up a little only when he reached the road. Heading to the house in which he'd been born.

The reunion with his mother was warm, moving, and electrified with emotions. When they spotted each other, neither of them said anything. They just embraced. The eyes of Ira McCoy were big and wet with tears. Her graying hair gave her the expression of wisdom and the beauty of a goddess. The wrinkles appeared on her tender complexion, but to Ethan she still seemed quite attractive. A pity nobody could enjoy her beauty.

Ira McCoy lived alone. Sarah and Benjamin Zachariah and Sarah's husband Jason used to visit her occasionally, and Peter came to have lunch with her at least three times a week. Although she lived alone, Ira McCoy was not a lonely person. With her friends and the memory of her late husband, she had no time to think about loneliness.

Ethan didn't stay long at home. He spent the evening there and stayed overnight, but intended to move on the next day. Montana waited for him, and the journey would be a long one. They talked about the years they hadn't seen each other. Ira showed him a pack of postcards she received from Will. The same ones Will sent to Ethan only with different content. Ethan asked his mother to give his regards to Will when he arrived home as she would see him sooner.

Ethan kept asking himself how long it would be before he would meet up with his brother again. The paths of their lives kept getting farther apart. It became more difficult for Ethan to fight the feeling of yet another loss. Soon he would be completely alone. He and his River. That would be his entire world until time indefinite.

He took leave of his mother and drove toward the mill. The harvesters hummed in the fields. The harvest was in the full swing.

He drove up to the mill and parked the car in front. Leaving

River to run about, he went to look for Peter. Peter was glad to see him, but he wasn't happy when Ethan said he was planning on moving on after only about an hour they spent together. He finished what he came for and didn't want to stay any longer. Peter was to report to a new owner from now on. Ethan had made a legal transfer of the mill to his brother. He did the same thing for Will as his father had done for him many years ago. With one difference. Will would need the mill more than Ethan. And Will would come back to Greenfield in a few years, maybe even sooner, while Ethan didn't know when *he* would return.

He had a snack in the Greenfield restaurant before he went to settle the last thing that still kept him in Greenfield. He came mostly for that reason before heading north. And it was something he was afraid of most.

Ethan needed a lot of courage to visit the Zachariah family.

And face the long-postponed encounter with the past.

Sarah Zachariah opened the door after he climbed onto the porch and knocked three times rather than ringing the bell. A porch swing hung motionless in the shade of the climbing roses that hid the surprise on her face before she returned his hello.

"Ethan! Hello. What a pleasant surprise. What are you doing here?"

"I'm passing by, so I dropped in to say hello and see how you're doing."

"Please, come in."

They didn't embrace or reach out with their hands.

"Thanks. Does the invitation extend to my friend too?" Ethan patted January River on the head. "Or shall I leave him to entertain himself in the garden?"

"The invitation goes to both of you. This house is always open for our four-legged friends, in case you forgot," she said, with a little smile.

"I didn't forget. How could I?"

"He's a nice dog." Sarah knelt before River. "Almost the same as Riv. I'd think it was him if I didn't know he. . . ." her voice trailed off.

"They are alike," Ethan said. "But this one is much more spoiled. Life in the city, I guess."

"Probably. What can I get you? Coffee? Tea? Lemonade?"

"Lemonade will be just fine, thank you." He sat at the kitchen table and looked at Sarah taking a jar of lemonade out of the refrigerator and filling two glasses.

"Sorry for bringing you into the kitchen, but it's the coolest place in the house. Hot as hell today."

She put the lemonades on the table and filled a small dish with water and gave it to River. The dog lapped eagerly.

"To say the least," Ethan said, looking at River emptying the dish. "The thermometer in my car went crazy."

"Not the best time for driving. Are you staying here for a while or you are going back to New York immediately?"

"Neither. I'm heading north. To Montana."

"Montana? Why there?"

"Plan to spend the summer. I'll rest. And write. Need to finish a book I started when Susan fell ill."

"I'm sorry about your wife, Ethan. I apologize for not calling or writing you a letter. It didn't seem quite right, somehow. We haven't seen each other for a long time and . . . you know."

"It's all right, Sarah. Thank you."

"That was her sitting beside you when you drove past the school that day?"

"Yes. Susan was with me."

"She was beautiful, as far as I could tell. I regret I didn't have the chance to get to know her."

"That's my fault. She liked Greenfield very much, but I brought her here on only three occasions. The first time she was working on a story about it. Then, when we came here after we married. The last time was when my father died. I wasn't much in the mood for introductions or socializing, I'm afraid. I could hardly wait to return to New York. I've made a mistake. I've made many. I know that now. I should've brought her more often. But I've had neither the need nor the desire to come. Can you understand that?"

"I'm sure you had your reasons. New York was home, and it makes sense that you spent more time there than here. I would've done the same."

"You're right. But it wasn't just New York. Something else stopped me. The memories. So much happened here—far too much—and I still have a mess in my head when I think of everything. I only told Susan how I felt through all these years. How difficult it was, how much I've suffered. I had nightmares. I couldn't sleep at night, couldn't pull myself together. That's why I left. I had to in order to take control of my life. Get on my own feet; I couldn't crawl on the stones of the past forever. I thought it would be much easier to start from scratch in new surroundings. To forget the past, leave it where it belongs, and carry on with my life."

"Did you succeed?"

"Very hard at first, but I gritted my teeth. Will was also there, and he helped me a lot to become independent. I would've returned, had it not been for him. And I would have solved nothing by doing that. I had no choice. I had to grit my teeth and fight or come back and fade away bit by bit. I decided to stay and fight."

"Are you sorry about that? Are you sorry you didn't return then?"

"No, I'm not. Slowly things improved. In only a few years I became so successful that I couldn't believe it myself. And I started out as a waiter. Everything was ideal, Sarah. So perfect, it seemed it would last for eternity. But then life decided I enjoyed it too much and said enough. It took from me what I loved most. History repeating itself. Overnight, I became a man without a goal and no future in which to look forward."

"Don't talk like that. Everything's going to work out just fine. We're strong, you know. We rise and fall so many times, but we always recover. That's why we survive."

"How did you recover after Der's and your mother's deaths? Sorry for asking you that, but I think I would have gone crazy if I were you."

"It was hard for me, Ethan. I have no words to describe how hard it was to return to the living. Every night I woke up, choking with pain, thinking I would die. I thought I'd burst because of the pressure I lived under. But I put one foot in front of the other like you did and continued to live. I had no choice. I needed to take care of Dad."

"How's Ben? I haven't seen him for ages. Ever since my father's funeral."

"He's doing fine, in his own way. He's rather run down, but that's not stopping him from helping those who need help even more. I think his little patients have pulled him out from the crisis he fell into after Mom's death. He's so devoted to them all. Where do you think he is now?"

Ethan smiled. "Your father's a wonderful man. I'll never forget what he did for Riv. I owe him so much. And I will for the rest of my life."

Sarah offered a melancholic smile as she looked at the dog lying stretched out on his belly on the kitchen floor cooling himself.

"That's why what happened to Derrick's so hard for me," Ethan continued. "That we didn't prevent it, somehow."

He managed to utter those words after all. And it was easier than he thought. He'd been so afraid of that moment, and it finally arrived. With no way to turn back now, he had to go to the end. He felt glad about that, in a way.

Sarah looked at him quizzically. "What do you mean, if we could have prevented it? Could anybody have known what would happen in advance?"

"No, nobody could've known. You're right. But I still think we could have done something. And we did nothing. That's what's been haunting me all those years. That's why I had to leave Greenfield because I couldn't have stood life here anymore. Sarah, I know how Derrick died."

A dead silence crept into the kitchen for a few moments. Then Sarah said: "Ethan, I know how Derrick died too. The whole of Greenfield knows what happened. Things happen.

Why don't we leave it behind? Let's leave Derrick in peace. We live for tomorrow, let's forget about the past."

"Sarah, I won't have my peace until I tell you the truth. I've been keeping this inside me for much too long, and I'm on the verge of insanity. I can't bear it anymore. I must tell you. I must tell you the truth."

"What is the truth, Et? The only truth is that Derrick's gone. Nothing else matters."

"It matters to me. At night while I sleep and during the day while I work, it matters to me. It matters to me because I think I could have done something, which I haven't."

He watched Sarah, who silently looked at him in return. He pushed away the glass of lemonade and reached out his hands to her.

"Please, listen to what I'm trying to tell you. I think you should know how your brother died. I think you should've learned about that a long time ago, but. . . ." He shrugged his shoulders helplessly.

"I'm listening," she said. Her only words while the peace softened every line of her face. Ethan's eyes rested on this calm face as he struggled for words with which to begin.

So, here we are. The long-anticipated moment had arrived. So much fear, many sleepless nights, and excruciating pain had accumulated over the years. He had just a few minutes to unleash the tangled mess, thus sending the tragic memory back to the past where it belonged and hopefully find peace.

And how he might find his peace. To make reconciliation with that time and, what is most important of all, with himself.

But how could he say everything that was in his heart without leaving anything out? How could he compose his confession so Sarah would understand and forgive? How was he to mend the broken thread of life—severed a long time ago—and one he'd been wanting to repair ever since?

Could he bind the broken ends and move on? Would he drink the cup of bitterness until it was empty, and the gall and the unbearableness of living spilled all over the Greenfield soil where those he loved so much lied and where those he still loves as much walk on? With no more room for postponement, would his future be reborn here and now? All of that depended upon the next minutes and the words he chose very carefully and with great caution. Ethan took a deep breath and exhaled slowly.

"The ruling the police made of Derrick's death was true. But only partly," he paused, sorting out the whirlpool of thoughts and sentiments which rose inside him. "Derrick drowned, Derrick fell off the bridge. But Derrick didn't intend to nor did he commit *suicide*. The police didn't know that at the time of his death, Derrick wasn't alone on the bridge. Will, Jason and I were there too."

Ethan closed his eyes and drifted back to the past, many years ago. When he opened them again, Sarah sat in the same position as before, as if nothing happened in the meantime. As if the time has stopped.

He continued as if in a trance.

"On that particular morning we got ready for rafting. We also thought of swimming, so we planned to spend the whole day on the river. We intended to return in the evening and not before. That was the official version for our parents and anybody else who asked where we were going. For you as well. We wanted to take you with us, but you were ill. That's why we decided not to tell you about our plans at all. Well, we didn't lie much to you since we did go swimming and rafting like we said. But we didn't tell you our plan also included diving off the bridge. That was a crazy thing to consider and it would've been better had we never thought of it. As it had turned out, it was a fatal decision for one of us. Even so, it affected all of us. We only wanted to have fun and to prove to ourselves we could do it."

Sarah seemed calm, unusually so considering what Ethan was telling her. Ethan noticed, but pushed the thought away. Should he allow his train of thoughts to swerve a bit, everything would end. And the whole purpose of his return would never be consummated. If that were the case, he should have drowned with Derrick that day.

"We tied the raft to the shrub under the bridge and climbed the bridge," he rushed to keep ahead of his thoughts, "Will, as the oldest, was the first to take off his pants and sneakers and strode the railing. My heart stopped beating when he disappeared from sight, but then we heard a splash. Riv ran to the shore barking at the water, and we hurried to the railing. Some thirty feet downstream, Will surfaced and waved to us. He yelled how great it was and kept waving to us, encouraging us to dive. Jason was next. He folded his clothes and stacked them beside Will's and dove off the bridge. We heard another splash, and several seconds later he surfaced. He swam to the bank screaming with joy. At that moment, Will waited on the raft for Derrick and me.

"Derrick and I undressed and went to the railing together. I remember how he slowly folded his clothes with great care. When he looked at me, I saw the fear in his eyes. I was afraid myself. I told him we would dive together if he wanted to. He accepted. I was already on the other side of the railing clutching the construction when Riv barked from behind, startling us. With one leg flung over the barrier and the other still on the ground, Derrick shivered. I called out to him to give me his hand, but he didn't listen. Petrified, he couldn't move at all. He fixed his gaze on Riv running around barking. Will and Jason yelled at us from below. I shouted to Derrick and he looked at me with eyes full of trepidation. I told him to give me his hand, that everything would be all right and we would dive together. Derrick clutched the railing, not wanting to let go. I had no other choice but to come for him. At that moment he shouted. Seeing what was happening, Will and Jason ran toward the bridge. I took a step toward Derrick and told him to lean against me and give me his hand. I assured him everything would be fine if he held my hand. He seemed to have composed himself a bit and believed me. I don't know. Everything happened in a flash. I held his hand for a second, but then I didn't. I heard the splash and saw the water closing over Derrick. I dove in after him.

"The cold water swallowed me instantly. I shuddered and sank further into the deep water before getting my bearings. When I surfaced, I searched for Derrick, but there was no sign of him. Will, Jason and River were running from the bridge toward the riverbank. I didn't know what was happening. They shouted that Derrick sunk, but had not surfaced. I finally realized what they were trying to tell me. I inhaled deeply and plunged under the water. I looked for Derrick, but in vain. I found no trace of him. We searched the riverbed for half an hour, and I've never been as tired in my life as then. I don't know where I gathered the strength to continue looking along the banks. Two hours passed before we gave up hope that Derrick would suddenly appear, alive. Either he got stuck somewhere, or the water carried him a long way downstream. We could only pray to God that he swam out somewhere and would return home alone later. We didn't know how to help him beyond what we already did.

"We pulled the raft out, although I have no idea how we managed. We left his clothes in the same spot on the bridge where Derrick stacked them. Our hope was that somebody would see them and suspect something bad happened. We were much too scared to think at all. We should have called for help right away, but we were afraid. Even if we had called for help, I don't believe it would have turned out any different. Never in my life was I as afraid as then. And never in my life have I felt so helpless. Eventually we decided to keep quiet about everything and never tell anyone what really happened. We promised each other that our secret would die with us. That none of us would ever tell the truth, for as long as we lived. But, as you see, the secret is no secret any longer. It couldn't endure. The truth had to come to the fore.

"Sarah, I want you to know a single day hasn't passed that I haven't thought of Derrick and what happened. I am very, very sorry about everything. I've atoned a thousand times and begged God for forgiveness, but it hasn't helped much. Now, I'm begging you to forgive me if you can. Having to live with this 'til the end of my life is a punishment enough."

Speechless, Sarah was as pale as a statue, her eyes full of tears. In her hand she tightly gripped an empty glass of lemonade with the drops of condensed water on the outside. She made slow circles with it on the table, breathing heavily.

"I thought it was going to hurt less after all these years. That it was going to be . . . easier. But it wasn't. Well, as I said, we cannot do anything about that. Derrick's gone, and we have to live with that. We must go on living, no matter how impossible that might seem."

Ethan couldn't believe his ears. He thought he hadn't heard her right, but the expression on Sarah's face said differently.

"Sarah, is that all you have to say? That we have to get over it and move on? After everything I told you? I don't understand."

"Do you have a better idea? Can you bring Derrick back? Tell me!"

"I don't, but . . . I expected you to storm at me. I thought you'd start screaming, crying, show some emotion. Anything! I was expecting anything, everything, but not this."

"Et, I did my crying and I don't intend to continue crying for the rest of my life. I can't afford that. I have a family to think of. I must think of them and their future. No matter how much I loved my brother, he's dead. Not I, not you or anybody else can change that."

River, drowsing on the kitchen floor, rose his head at the sound coming from the corridor. He wagged his tail when a girl of some six or seven years appeared at the door. He approached her, his tail still swinging in a friendly way. Ethan jumped up from the table, pushing his chair away.

"Mommy," the girl exclaimed. "Look how nice he is." She embraced the dog who sniffed her and licked her face.

Sarah gazed at Ethan with a serious expression on her face.

"It's okay. He won't hurt her. He loves children."

"Amy, who told you to get out of bed? You know what the doctor told you? You have to lie down."

"But, Mommy—"

"Nothing, Mommy. Go back to your room." She took her by the hand.

"Who is that?" Amy hadn't moved from where she stood.

"That's my childhood friend. We haven't seen each other for a long time. He came to visit us."

"What's his name?"

"His name's Ethan. Now that you got to know each other you can go back to your bed."

"This is your dog?" Amy patted Riv's head.

"Yes, this is my dog," Ethan watched Amy with the same curiosity.

"He's very nice. Mommy, will you buy me a dog like this? I wish I had one."

"Maybe, when you grow older and if you'll be a good girl and return to your bed at once."

"But I'd like to have him now. Ethan, will you visit us again with. . . ." she stopped, not knowing the dog's name.

"River. His name is River. January River."

Sarah looked at him questioningly.

"Mommy, his name is the same as our river!"

"Yes, sweetie. But, you're still not in bed."

"Will you and January River visit us again?"

"Well, I don't know. Perhaps. Probably."

"When?"

"After I finish something. I'm going on a trip and won't be back for some time."

"For long? Are you going to be away a long time?"

"Amy, that will do," Sarah took her up in her arms. "Don't bug Uncle Ethan. Say goodbye and wish him a pleasant trip."

"I wish you a pleasant trip." She sent him a kiss.

"Goodbye, Amy," he sent a kiss to her before Sarah carried her away to her room.

"Forgive her for being so curious," Sarah said, upon returning to the kitchen. "Nothing goes unnoticed by her. She's a real pistol."

"How old is she?"

"Five. I can't bring myself to think of what it'll be like when she's eighteen."

"She's charming. When I spotted her, I thought I must be hallucinating. She looks so much like you when you were small."

"That you almost overturned that chair."

They both laughed.

"Everybody tells me that," Sarah spoke first. "I'm afraid that's hardly a compliment to her."

"Nonsense, Sarah. You're a very attractive woman. I think you are aware of that."

"Thank you, if that's what you think. But I wasn't attractive as a girl."

"Who is attractive at that age? Just skin and bones."

"You were attractive."

Ethan ignored her compliment as if he hadn't heard it. "Is that your only child?" he asked.

"I have a son too, Matthew. He's ten. Thank God, he's at school right now. While I have to look after that little rascal."

"I bet he's a good student."

"The best in his class."

"That sounds familiar somehow."

"There's something he inherited from me. Otherwise, he's all his dad."

"If you allow me to make a remark as an old friend, I never knew you and Jason liked each other. I was surprised when I heard of the two of you got married."

Sarah paused for a moment, and then answered, "Well, we weren't in love back then. I came to love him only later. After we were already married, that is."

Stunned, Ethan asked, "Why did you marry him, then?"

"He proposed to me."

"He proposed to you?"

"Yes, he proposed to me. And I accepted."

"Only because he proposed to you?"

"Ethan, Jason's a good man. I always knew that. And you

know it too. Life's never been easy for him. But it seems as if it left no scars on him. He's good, faithful, attached, tender, and above all, honest. He adores me. And I love him. Some things take time. You have to try it to realize whether or not it's for you."

"And so, you test-married Jason Hawk, and it turned out well."

"Spoken like that, it may look that way."

"What would've happened if somebody else proposed to you? You would've test-married him too? What would've happened, for example, if I had proposed to you?"

"But you never proposed to me. That's the big difference."

"No, I didn't. But I'd still like to know."

"There're things in life we shall never know the answers."

"Exactly. Perhaps it's better that way. Anyway, I'm glad you're happy and you're doing well. I mean it."

"Thank you. We're fine for now. Jason works as a lawyer in Scottsbluff. He has his office there. Did you know he got his degree from Creighton University in Omaha?"

"I never knew that."

"He was among the best in his class. One would think he'd deal with big cases, earning big money. But no, not him. Jason Hawk made up his mind to do small, petty cases and lawsuits and represent ordinary people. We argued about that in the beginning. He took cases when he wouldn't even take money from his clients. Especially when they were poor or in debt. He told them there wasn't much work to their lawsuit and they could pay him the next time. As for the nights he stayed up pondering their cases and I stayed awake with him, everything was for free. He came to his senses in time. But he never renounced his mercy completely."

"That sounds like Jason. I could hardly see him in a different light."

"People like him. They really do. Thanks to his honesty, he was never short of business and we were never short of money. As little as he charged, we'd still get by. As if some angel watched over him and us. He's at work now. He called half an hour before you came and said he'd be late. Something kept him."

"Isn't it tedious to drive back and forth to Scottsbluff every day?"

"To Jason? On the contrary, he enjoys that. He likes to be on the move. Remember how he used to be crazy about horses?"

Ethan nodded.

"It's the same today. Except that he has replaced horses with the car."

"That's progress, yeah."

"It wasn't always like that, Et. We weren't happy all the time like we are now. I'm ashamed to have to say it, but it's the truth. It was all my fault. Half a year before Matthew was born, I almost divorced Jason."

Ethan sipped the lemonade Sarah poured again in his glass. He put the glass on the table and looked into her eyes expecting an explanation.

"I know I reacted like a fury and rashly when Jason confided in me. I should've grasped it, I should've understood, and I was so stupid. Ethan, Jason told me about your secret."

Ethan turned over the glass he still held in his hand and the lemonade spilled all over the table.

Sarah jumped to fetch a dishtowel and wiped the lemonade before it dripped on the floor. January River also jumped, startled by the sudden commotion in the kitchen.

Ethan couldn't utter a word. The words were all stuck in his throat.

"I was raving like a lunatic when he confessed that." Sarah wiped the table clean. Calmed and seeing that nothing major was going on, River stretched out on the floor again. "I've been a real witch. I threatened to divorce him. I said a lot of nasty words to him. I called all three of you some strong names. I shouted that he was a killer. Then I broke down." She put the dishtowel on the washing basin and sat back beside Ethan. "I cried and Jason took me in his arms. He kept stroking me, and he didn't say a word. When I asked him what he thought I should do, should I report it to the police, he answered, 'Whatever you do will be the right thing. I'll understand.' That's all he said, and it was the turning point in our relationship. I understood what kind of person Jason really was. And I realized I loved him. His love for me was beyond question, anyway.

"That's the only crisis we had in our marriage. For some time, I had doubts whether Jason married me because of his sense of duty and the feelings of guilt—to make it up to Derrick, you know. But then Matthew came, and I knew Jason not only loved me, but was also in love with me. Luck smiled upon me."

She put her hand over Ethan's and gently squeezed it.

"Ethan, dear, I have nothing to forgive you because there's nothing to hold against you. Not you, nor Will or Jason. It was an accident. The same could have happened to any of the three of you, and it would have been none the easier about it. Because I loved all of you the same."

Ethan felt the tightening in his chest. He found himself on the bridge above the January River again. He saw the water swallow Derrick for the umpteenth time. The intensity of that tightening grew, making itself ever more difficult to bear. He looked into Sarah's tender eyes and whispered a barely audible *thank you*. He looked into the eyes which mirrored all the greatness of love which once burned in the heart of Derrick Zachariah. But those were the eyes of his sister now.

After all they had been through, the Zachariah family still knew only about love.

And Sarah, as before, knew how to keep secrets.

Sarah's hand still held Ethan's when he smiled at her.

In that touch, which meant to him more than all the spoken words, Ethan McCoy found reconciliation. Reconciliation with himself and with the Zachariah family. And finally, reconciliation with life he had longed for so much.

The touch of a hand was reconciled with the touch of another's hand.

The last thing Derrick felt before his life was interrupted

was the touch of his friend's hand. The hand that didn't hold back, but let him precipitate into death instead.

What returned Ethan's right to live and hope in a more tranquil and happier future was the touch of Sarah's hand. The touch of forgiveness, understanding, and love.

Accumulated sorrow poured out, and the cup remained empty. The burden had been divided, the past buried.

Derrick found his peace, and so did Ethan along with him. In the touch of a hand.

He brought her hand to his lips and kissed it. "Thank you, Sarah, for this conversation. It meant so much. Though the pain is still there, at least I'll be able now to continue my trip with more peace of mind."

"You're leaving already? Won't you stay for a bit longer?"

"Unfortunately, I should be going."

"I'd like you to stay for supper. There are so many things we should still talk about. You told me nothing of how you liked New York, how you spent your time there. How's Will? Where is he now?"

"I don't know exactly. I don't know whether he's still on the seas or on the land. Perhaps he was fired, I'm not sure."

"Something happened?"

"It's a long story. I'd rather not talk about it now. It wouldn't surprise me if you see him in Greenfield soon too."

"I'd really like that."

"Well, I should be off now. The journey's waiting."

"And supper? You won't change your mind? Jason will be sorry to have missed you. So will Dad. Dad should be here any moment. I'm sure Matthew would like to see you too. And, I'd also like you to stay. I'd like you to tell me more about you and your wife."

"Now, you've put me in an awkward position. I feel bad about it, but I'll have to decline your offer. I didn't plan anything like this. I'd like to get on my way as soon as possible. You won't be angry with me, will you?"

"Sarah Zachariah's never angry with her friends, no matter

how stubborn they may be."

"You know what? I promise, the next time I come I'll drop by just for your sake and stay for supper. And we'll talk everything over for as long as we wish. I'll tell you about Susan then. Susan was a wonderful person and I could talk to you about her for days. You meet such a person only once, twice in your lifetime at most. She reminded me of you in a way."

"Thank you." Sarah got lost for a moment at the unexpected compliment, but recovered fast. "I'll hold you to your word, Ethan McCoy. It'll be a great joy for all of us when you come back again."

"For me too, Sarah. A great joy."

"Can you hold on a minute? I'll be right back."

"Okay." Accompanied by January River, he moved to the door while Sarah disappeared up the stairs.

"I nearly forgot," she said, gasping when she caught up with him in the yard. "Matthew would never forgive me if he knew you were here and hadn't left your autograph for him."

She reached out with a copy of his first novel.

"That's his dearest," she shrugged. "He says it's *cool* and *one hell of a book* and that it really makes sense. I don't know where he picked up those expressions. We don't teach them that in our school."

Ethan laughed and wrote a short dedication.

"Well, Sarah, I wish you all the best. Thanks for the lemonade and for the talk. Please give my love to Jason and your father. As for Matthew, tell him we'll meet next time. Then he will get a complete interview if he'd like."

"What should I tell him, when will that be? He'll be a nuisance for days about that."

"Tell him, in a year's time. Maybe sooner."

"In a year's time??"

"It'll pass quickly, Sarah. Believe me."

"Will I get the answer also to the mystery then?" She cast a glance at the golden retriever. "*January River?* Ethan McCoy, I think you still owe me a lot of explanations."

"Certainly. Next time we meet, there'll be no more secrets between us."

"Sure?"

"Dead sure. The light of the truth will swallow the dark secrets of the heart."

Before they left Greenfield, Ethan took River to the clearing from where he used to watch sunsets. Taking a bend at too high a speed, he braked sharply and pulled up. But this time there was no place for panic in his heart. He met his friend with a smile. Derrick smiled too as he did in the happiest of their days. His laughter spread all over Greenfield like an echo before it disappeared for good.

Before he regained his senses, three boys dashed in front of Ethan accompanied by screaming and overjoyed laughter. Had he not pulled up instantly, he would have hit them almost certainly. One of them sped on his skateboard while the other two followed on their Rollerblades. They wore Dickies and Homeboy trousers, marine-blue DC Collin McKay skateboarding shoes, Foundation T-shirts and baseball caps turned backwards. Backpacks jumped on their backs.

Ethan smiled at the sight. Unusual for Greenfield, but what he saw many times in the streets of New York City. He found it impossible not to connect this scene to one visit that took place many years ago and everything that followed as a result of it. "The Summer in Greenfield" was bearing its fruits.

"You see, my old friend," he turned to the dog, "even Greenfield isn't what it used to be."

Greenfield followed the fashion of the big cities in its slow manner.

The sunset was as beautiful as in the days of his childhood and that hadn't changed as far as Greenfield was concerned.

When the sun set completely, Ethan switched on the headlights of his Rover and headed north.

Toward the Big Sky Country that was already sleeping, but also waited for him.

23

than rented a house situated on the slope high above
Flathead Lake. A deep forest of larch, lodgepole pine,
ponderosa pine, western white pine, and ponderosa or
western yellow pine protected it from the traffic noise, murmurs
and curious looks of the passersby, as well as the music from
jukeboxes and cafés. A porch facing the lake with mountains
beyond it, provided a perfect place for Ethan's work. The peaceful surroundings with plenty of water and breathtaking nature
was home to beavers, bears, mule deer, moose, elks, muskrats,
and minks. Ethan thought he could stay forever. But he also
knew that wouldn't be possible. Though no longer young, he
felt deep inside that the future still had surprises in store for him.
He wasn't ready to settle down for good yet. The very reason
why he decided to stay here for a while, with no deadlines and
no firm plans. He may even call his mother and ask her to move
in with him. The air of the high mountains might do her a world
of good.

He drove with January River to Dayton for supplies. Ethan
didn't need much food. He worked hard and ate little. But even
if he intended to be an ascetic, he couldn't ask his friend to make
the same sacrifice. That would be unfair.

In line for the cashier at the grocery store, a voice addressed him from behind. He turned around and saw the smiling face of an old lady. She couldn't be more than her mid-seventies or early eighties at the most.

"Good evening, young man. How are you? I haven't seen you in town for quite some time."

"Good evening." He recognized the lady who gave him a copy of the Watchtower publication titled, "Will There Ever Be an End to Sufferings?" "I'm fine, thanks for asking. I work a lot, so I don't have much time to come down to the town. How are you?"

"Very well. Considering my age, very well. What do you occupy yourself with, if you don't mind my asking?"

"I'm finishing my manuscript for my next book."

"Indeed? What book?"

"It's a novel. Somewhat autobiographical."

Ethan waited for the girl at the cashier to work out the sum and produce the receipt.

"Is it your first novel?"

"Well, not exactly. I've written several. This is the fourth."

"Really. What did you say your name was?"

"I didn't. But I'm Ethan McCoy."

The eyes of the young girl working at the cashier went wide in recognition and her mouth pulled into a broad smile. Ethan was convinced that the whole of Dayton—if it wasn't the case already—would learn within the next couple of hours that a renowned author was in town. He didn't mind that, provided he still had the privacy he needed to continue converting his thoughts into a story. His life story.

"I haven't heard of you," the old lady retorted. "I'm sorry."

"Doesn't matter," Ethan showed understanding. "Many haven't."

The cashier obviously didn't agree with her because her face turned into a grimace of reproach. *Where have you been living, madam, not having heard of Ethan McCoy.*

Ethan collected the change from the girl who was all

kindness and waited for the old lady to pay for her groceries.

"Allow me," he offered his help, taking her things.

"Oh, that's very nice of you, Ethan. May I call you Ethan?"

"Of course. That's my name."

"Mine is Marion."

"Nice to meet you, Marion. Do you live far? Can I give you a lift?"

"Thanks a lot, but that would be too much. You're most kind. I live nearby, the second street around the corner. The fourth house on the right."

"If you change your mind, I'm still here."

"Thank you. But, would you like to drop by for a cup of tea? We could have a cozy chat."

"I hope you won't mind, but my dog's waiting for me in the car. He had nothing to eat since morning. I was so into my manuscript I forgot about his food. Some other time, perhaps?"

"My door's always open for you, Ethan, any time. You can bring your wife along if you're married."

"I was married. Susan died four months ago."

"I'm sorry to hear that. Death's an unspeakable loss, especially if you love someone dearly. I've been without my husband for twenty years now. It's not much easier for me now than it was when he died. But I put my trust in God and I have hope I shall see him again when he's resurrected. That gives me the strength to stand up to that loss. Do you believe in God?"

"I do. That's how I've been brought up. My family was very religious."

"You're a lucky man. Not everyone has the hope we have."

"That's the way it probably is, Marion." He didn't mention, however, that he had neglected his God a little lately. "Now, you must excuse me. I'm in a hurry, and the sun's about to set soon. I don't like to miss that."

"You like to watch sunsets?"

"Absolutely. They're especially beautiful here in Montana."

"Then we shall have another subject for our conversation when you come for tea."

"I look forward to it."

"Don't forget: the second street on the left, the fourth house on the right."

"I won't forget. Goodbye."

"Good night, Ethan."

He sat in a rocking chair and sipped a soda. The sun was setting behind the mountain peaks. The light it cast on the nearby forest and the porch from which Ethan and January River watched its descent waned steadily. The colors of the sky spilled in the nuances of the rainbow and reminded Ethan of a phenomenon that took place a long time ago.

He stopped rocking and waited. His hair stood up.

The colors became intense, bright and warm, and then it happened.

The light spilled all over the sky.

The sun sank behind the mountains.

Ethan dropped into the rocking chair.

January River whined and pricked up his ears.

The silence reigned everywhere. Then the forest let its sounds be heard.

It was the blue flash.

"The green light resulted from an interaction between the sun's light and the earth's atmosphere. When the outer rim of the sun sinks behind the horizon, its light breaks apart into the spectrum just as a rainbow does—with the red light at the bottom and the blue one at the top. As the sun descends further so does the red color, and the blue disperses into the atmosphere. And at that moment, the last fraction of the visible light may flash in the green color."

"How do you—?" Ethan tried to understand what he just heard. "How do you know all that?"

"Mr. Harper explained it. He knows almost everything about the stars there is to know."

"Did he?"

"That's a rare phenomenon. The sky has to be very clear to make it possible for the green flash to happen."

Why is it called green when the blue one disperses into the atmosphere?"

"That's because green is the other primary color of the light."

"Huh?"

"Don't worry. There is the blue flash as well. It's even more beautiful than the green one. But the odds are against the chance of you ever seeing it."

"Why?"

"Because the atmosphere must be very, very, very clear and enough blue light has to penetrate the sky to cause the blue flash to appear."

24

The novel *Dark Secrets of the Heart* by Ethan McCoy was published in the fall of 1996. From the first day it charged unstoppably toward number one. It remained there for about twenty weeks, and it didn't leave the top of the best-selling fiction until the end of the following year. Its copyrights were sold in twenty-five countries, and its success has returned the glory and glamor to Ethan's earlier books.

The critics compared *Dark Secrets of the Heart* with *The Bridges of Madison County*, which had attracted similar attention four years ago. But this time the glory went to the others. Robert Kincaid and Francesca Johnson were no stars anymore.

Those that shone like meteors were:

Jason Hawk as Trevor Stephens,

Derrick and Sarah Zachariah as Joshua and Debra Dickerman,

Susan Dupie as Catherine Dubois,

William Patrick McCoy as Paul Thomas MacKenzie,

Ethan McCoy as Jonathan MacKenzie and

January River as River.

The only difference was their shine did last much longer than that of a meteor.

Ethan McCoy still lives in Dayton, Montana. His mother moved in with him and her only worry was to take care of the nourishment for her negligent son. But soon she became nostalgic about Greenfield, and when Ethan went to pay the first visit to the Zachariahs, she returned with him.

Ethan met Matthew Hawk and gave him an evening-long interview. After a long time, he also saw his old friends Jason and Ben Zachariah—that old, good-hearted man, now well-advanced in years. He stayed for supper, as he had promised.

And uncovered all the secrets.

At parting, he left a present with his friends. His newest book, still fresh off the press, and with the following dedication:

For all that life has given us,
and everything it took from us.
You are always in my heart,
Ethan

Like cuddling a newborn baby, Sarah took it and pressed it tenderly against her heart. Then she kissed Ethan.

For everything he gave them.

After almost twenty years of traveling around the world, William Patrick McCoy left the seas for good. The last harbor from which his ship put to sea was Cherbourg. He then returned to Greenfield and spent the rest of his life there. He never married.

The January River flowed the same way, even after twenty years, carrying memories with it. The past ones, the present ones, and those yet to be born. It washed the banks of this simple and tame town, supplying them with life. It watered the rich soil and painted it green.

In the darkness of the night and under the shine of the moonlight, two bodies broke its still surface rising from its depths. A man and a dog. The splashing echoed through the night.

A shout disturbed the quietness of the world, followed by the barking of the dog.

"January River, catch me."

The water splashed in millions of dancing droplets before everything fell silent again.

Did you like my story? If your answer is yes, please follow me on Twitter, @BernardJanWorld, and tweet what you think. Don't forget to include #JanuaryRiver. Say hi, and I promise I'll respond.

Please continue reading now and find bonuses you may like.

Acknowledgements

I wrote this book out of love for the American dream, a great American novel and New York City.

A big thank you I owe to the following people for helping me with it. After my Croatian publisher Goran Pavletić and Epifanija, Dragan Tomaševski was the first to begin with me my English adventure by showing patience and endurance while we worked on the first draft of its English translation. I know it was not always easy to meet my requests and accept my many interventions. My beta readers Irena James Mokos, Thomas Carley Jr., and Maks Andrijanovs gave me valuable input and comments for its improvement. Trish Reeb did a hard editing part, Tina Mari Combs cleared up what was still wrapped in the fog of my grammatical misunderstanding, while Word Refiner from wordrefiner.com refined every word you've read. I cannot and must not forget to give thanks to the two awesome indie authors, Jonathan Hill and Michael Evans, who helped me with my blurb; my book cover designer Domi at Inspired Cover Designs and all of you who helped me pick it; my parents, Ksenija and Dubravko, and my late grandmother, Anđelka, whose song of nightingales I still sometimes hear, as distant echoes from my childhood days.

And you, my darling, my beloved cat, Marcel. You will always be here with me.

As bloodstream carries life through us, silent waters of the January River will carry memories of you. Until its banks run dry and there is no more.

I love you all.

BJ

Share What You Love
(About the Author)

If you liked my writing and enjoyed reading my novel *January River*, please visit my website where you can find other books I wrote and stay in touch with me by subscribing to my mailing list, reading my blog Muse or just emailing with me.

www.bernardjan.com

I encourage you to also check my two novellas *A World Without Color* and *Look for Me Under the Rainbow*, my next-to-be published books in English and those already published in Croatian.

Besides being obsessed with reading and writing books, I'm also an animal rights advocate and environmentalist. Helping others and spreading kindness, love and empathy toward every living creature plays important role in my life.

If I'm your kind of guy, you are welcome to connect with me and follow me on my favorite social networks: Twitter, Goodreads and LinkedIn.

There is no greater joy than to share what you love with

those who appreciate it.

Thanks for your time, love and support!

BJ

Reviews

Thank you for reading *January River* and spending, I hope, a few quality hours with it. Please consider leaving an honest review on Amazon and Goodreads. It doesn't have to be long. Even a sentence or two makes a huge difference and I will appreciate them.

I'm sure you know how much indie authors depend on you. You're the reason why we write and publish, strive to improve and do our best.

Your honest review generates a beacon of light to other readers seeking books to enjoy. Books that take them elsewhere, into different worlds and other lives, as they get lost between their pages.

Thank you for that. Thank you for sharing our stories.

Please also leave your honest review for *A World Without Color* and *Look for Me Under the Rainbow* on Amazon.

Acclaim for Bernard Jan

A WORLD WITHOUT COLOR

"When the writing is this good, the mind travels through space and time and the heart follows."

—Olivier Delaye, author of *The Forgotten Goddess*

"The writing style of the author is simply beautiful; honest, poetic and full of emotions . . . I knew from the beginning that it will be an emotional, heartbreaking story, but I was impressed how the author managed to transmit also some of his thoughts and I do applaud him for the strong messages."

—Nico J. Genes, author of *Magnetic Reverie, Reverie Girl, LESSONS in LIFE: Achieving a better you through self-reflection* and *ADHD: LIFE IS BEAUTIFUL*

"A book that will exercise your heart strings as it is brimming with emotions. Keep that box of tissues close. Recommend it."

—Wilbur Seymore, author of *War/Peace 2036* and *Living Word*

"This sweet autobiographical novella will pull your heart strings all the way through."

—Adam Webling, YA blogger and aspiring writer of YA

and TV

"His words and imagery are stellar . . . honestly . . . he captures all those emotions pet-parents go through trying to rationalize our decisions, understand the whys, convince ourselves we will be okay, and determine how or if we can lean on anyone around us. By showcasing Marcel's movements and struggles, we see the pain Jan's family has gone through. It is visceral and constant. It is harsh and definitive. It is widespread and menacing."

—James J. Cudney, author of *Watching Glass Shatter*, *Father Figure* and *Braxton Campus Mysteries* series

LOOK FOR ME UNDER THE RAINBOW

"Every once in a while, an author comes along who wears their heart on their sleeve and pours it onto the pages of a book. If you haven't read anything by Bernard Jan, you are missing an opportunity to feel his words to your very soul . . . I fell in love with Danny and his exuberance, not unlike that of a human child and I found myself lost in this warm tale turned nightmare turned call to action for the world."

—Dianne Bylo, review writer for Tome Tender

"Bernard Jan does a superb job, because his prose is poetic and enjoyable, and even the dark moments have a special quality to it—the quality that comes with knowing that the power to change the world is in our hands."

—Dario Cannizzaro, author of *Of Life, Death, Aliens and Zombies* and *Dead Men Naked*

"Bernard Jan's writing delivers such imagery that pictures aren't needed. I cringed at times with some of the details, but it's the truth that must be told so that more will be aware, and in turn we can discover how to help."

A World Without Color
Extract

You curl up in your new hideout, and the soft light of the April afternoon washes your worn-out body. You are aware of my closeness. You confirm that with a gentle sigh while my palm tenderly slides down your fur. You still like my touch, although pain is what you now mostly feel. And uncertainty—but for how long?

Against the tracksuit pants I wipe a lock of your hair which is stuck to my palm. I try to take a better position, crawling next to you under the table. I hate the sentimentality of people who want to capture with photos the beautiful moments in life because they believe that's the only way they can remain part of their memories. Ironic, because I myself resort to this now. Nothing else is left for me. Another day, week, month at best is the most optimistic prognosis.

Only this time. I will make an exception.

Your chest is rising and falling, fighting for every breath. It's not easy for you, I know, and I would love most if I could breathe for you. But I can't. Even if I breathe a new life into you, it probably wouldn't help. You wouldn't even let me. Because you are a fighter. Besides, it seems to me you don't like people taking pity on you, as you didn't like it when they laughed in your face. This is why I control myself when I'm around you, poorly disguising the true nature of my feelings in a lame attempt to preserve your dignity. Panic hits me because of what is coming!

A tidal wave rushes from within, forcing tears to my eyes, which stream silently down my face and drip-drop onto your colorful blanket. Jolly green, purple and beige squares support your long, thin and distorted body like a gentle cloud. The shadow of what you used to be.

I support myself on my elbows, taking the first snapshot with my cell phone in my left hand. You hear a click and crack open your eyes. Your gaze rests on me, warming me with the heat of the hearth fire that fades away. I take another picture, producing another click, and then my hand trembles; I have to dry the tears that, undecided, stop and pause in the corners of my eyes.

You raise your head, not ceasing to look at me. Your good eye caresses my soul, while the other, sick from cataracts and inflammation unsuccessfully treated with ointments and drops, looks into the unknown. I'm stroking your hair, matted around it, waiting for you to be ready to continue our little photo session.

Again you accept me and indulge my whim. Gently as a newborn, you push your head along my hand, responding to my caress. First you rub your little nose into my fingers, and then you push your left ear against my hand, wanting me to scratch and massage it. When you become bored or you think it is enough, with amazing vigor you start to wash yourself. You surprise me a little because I don't remember when was the last time I saw you wash yourself. (It was a long time ago, just as eons have gone by since the days when you would happily nestle in the most comfortable seat in the apartment, after successfully sponging an abundant meal, and start to clean yourself. An invisible clock, or timer in you—as we used to joke—woke you up and led you, with your tail raised, to your bowls, where you patiently waited until, usually Mom, capitulated before your determination and persistence of the winner.) I smile, encouraged by a false hope and strong mental images awakened from the past. How little it takes for the Phoenix to resurrect in me and clatter the wings of joy. How dishonest I am with myself (and you) and subject to self-deception!

I leave you for a moment and hurry into the kitchen to show the photos to Mom. You continue sprucing up, as you know it's time for Saša's arrival. As always, you want to show yourself to him in the best light. You care about what Saša thinks of you. I don't think you do this so he can pet you and lavish words of praise on you, calling you Viola, Love. No, you accept Saša because you know you will be better each time you see him and you want to give something back to him. You want to show him that his visits really make you feel better. And so you do that. I don't know with which words I can express more clearly what I feel for you, so I will repeat: *Viola, my love.*

My thoughts come rushing back like raging currents of mountain rivers that do not stop for anything or anyone. Hurrying with a roar to their finish line, completely self-sufficient. Each word I make immortal here must be engraved with the dedication of a blind stonemason who, just by sense of touch and guided by indestructible faith, creates from the shapeless mass a work which present generations, but also those who come after, will admire. Those who are alive today, and their children who are just born, setting the foundation for new generations. This is our written monument and I snuggle up against it, blinded by the pain inflicted upon me by every minute that takes us into the future. The future is what I want to avoid at any cost, selfishly keeping the present so these moments last as long as possible. Not thinking about you and the relief it will bring you. We are both on the road of no return. Do you think so too? Do you also feel at least a fraction of regret we will part soon, with no guarantee and no promise that, in the blink of an eye or the distant future, we might meet each other again? Tell me, dearest. . . .

Please leave your honest review on Amazon.

Look for Me Under the Rainbow
Extract

The sea was unusually calm, even the deep currents seemed to stand still. As if suspended in the hushed stillness of dawn. The blue darkness of the night sky began to recede as the pale daylight washed over the horizon. Helped by the frail rays of the wintry sun shimmering through a cloud of fog. In the cold air, the coat woven out of the drops evaporated from the sea, turned into small crystals of ice.

The fog crept along the surface of the sea, dragging like a tired traveler, and spread in the direction of the land. Thin in places, thick in others, it occasionally revealed a glimpse of the blinding whiteness that covered most of the land.

If you looked at the right moment, when patches of fog dispersed enough to reveal an endless vista, you could see that it was, in fact, not land. Enveloped by the gradually disappearing fog, huge icebergs loomed, huddled atop the ice crust covering the sea of blue. At first glance, one might easily mistake them for a continent. It did, in fact, exist. The outline of the coast etched against the distant horizon was all part of nature's optical trick to fool a casual observer. Swathed in a mist of crystals, countless icebergs of various sizes stacked next to each other merged into the image of an ice mountain. The anomaly, carried by deep but weak currents, traveled the ocean almost imperceptibly.

If not for the sound of the icebergs clashing and breaking piercing the sleepy air, the entire scene would appear lifeless. A white wasteland. Even the scattered groups of seals dozing lazily on white sheets of ice, seemed motionless and almost unreal. Their dark, slick bodies struck a sharp contrast with the surrounding harmony of whiteness. As if they were unwanted intruders. Now and then a seal would move, usually a female. With a sharp sudden spasm, one cried out in pain struggling to bring a new life into this icy world of cruel beauty.

Having left her group, she lay on her side trying to find the most comfortable position to endure the labor pains. Growing stronger and more frequent, they produced searing pain. She felt the restless pup kick and strain to come out into a whole new world. A world of breathtaking beauty, yet fraught with danger. She wanted to help it. She matched the pace of her breathing with his efforts to break the thin membrane that divided him from the outer world. She synchronized her heartbeat with his, but to no avail.

She knew it was going to be a difficult birth. Still not full term, her offspring was in a hurry to leave her body. She nevertheless hoped the two of them would somehow succeed.

When the pup suddenly started to writhe and push inside her, she could not help howling in pain. Her cry resounded over the ice, eclipsing the muted groans of other mothers-to-be who were to begin labor in a few days. They were rested and ready, prepared for the hardship of giving birth, while she had only just arrived and was still exhausted after the long swim from the north. A journey she would again take several months from now with her pup, back home to the winter-bound land of eternal snow and ice. That is, *if* the birth went well and all ended happily.

As time went by, her fears seemed well founded. The last obstacle that separated her baby from the outer world was removed. Splashes of red blood stained the ice around her, slowly freezing in the bitter cold. But the pup still did not come. Not moving, exhausted and weary, it braced itself for another attempt.

She wondered whether it was male or female. If a male, would he look like his father who had just woken and proudly sniffed the air? If a female, would she, like her mother, one day have to go through this pain to bring her baby into the world? After carrying it lovingly inside her womb for months and months, only to. . . .

A new wave of excruciating pain slashed through her body and interrupted her thoughts. The pup pushed its way into the world, this time with more force and determination. The mother again synchronized all her bodily functions with its efforts to break free. Though united in their struggle, she wondered whether they felt the same pain. Or if only she suffered? Though it did not matter. She would gladly endure all the pain it took, if only to let it live.

As cry after piercing cry woke up other seals, they grew agitated, particularly the females about to become mothers in a few days. They timidly lifted their small heads to listen to the cries until they gradually abated. And then, one by one, they softly stretched on the ice that glistened in the sun. Silence fell, and everything was again hushed and motionless.

Please leave your honest review on Amazon.

Made in the USA
Middletown, DE
14 March 2022

62637038R00129